U0925182

别忘了我看不到我自己，我的角色仅限于看向镜子里的那个人。

Don’t forget that I cannot see myself that my role is limited to being the one who looks in the mirror.

那些触动我心扉的故事

李影／编译

江苏人民出版社

图书在版编目（CIP）数据

那些触动我心扉的故事：英汉对照 / 李影编译 . -- 南京：江苏人民出版社，2016.1
ISBN 978-7-214-17084-2

Ⅰ . ①那… Ⅱ . ①李… Ⅲ . ①英语—汉语—对照读物 Ⅳ . ① H319.4

中国版本图书馆 CIP 数据核字（2015）第 311091 号

书　　名　那些触动我心扉的故事：英汉对照
编 译 者　李　影
责任编辑　朱　超
装帧设计　浪殿设计　飞　扬
版式设计　张文艺
出版发行　凤凰出版传媒股份有限公司
　　　　　江苏人民出版社
出版社地址　南京市湖南路1号A楼，邮编：210009
出版社网址　http://www.jspph.com
　　　　　http://jsrmcbs.tmall.com
经　　销　凤凰出版传媒股份有限公司
印　　刷　北京中印联印务有限公司
开　　本　718 毫米 ×1000 毫米 1/16
印　　张　12
字　　数　135 千字
版　　次　2016 年 5 月第 1 版　2016 年 5 月第 1 次印刷
标准书号　978-7-214-17084-2
定　　价　24.00元

The Stories Touching My Heart

那些触动我心扉的故事

目 录 | CONTENTS

岁月如歌的光阴

静谧动人的声音

震撼非凡的身影

浮生若梦的幻影

岁月如歌的光阴

Life's best lessons are learned by living.

人生最好的启示来自于生活。

A Day at the Tradition

传统赛的一天

◎ Christine Clifford

Several years ago I was diagnosed with cancer. It was the most difficult time I have ever faced. I think it was my sense of humor that allowed me to hold onto my **sanity**[1]. Like many people who have gone through chemotherapy, I lost all of my hair and I was bald as a cue ball. I always had enjoyed wearing hats, so when my hair deserted me, I ordered several special hats with the hair already attached. It was easy and I never had to worry about how my hair looked.

I have always been a big golf fan. In fact, I have been to twenty-three straight U.S. Opens. At one point during my cancer treatments, my husband John and I decided to get away from the cold Minnesota winter and took a trip to Scottsdale, Arizona. There was a Senior PGA Tour event called The Tradition being played, and that seemed like just the ticket to lift my spirits.

The first day of the tournament brought out a huge gallery. It was a beautiful day, and I was in heaven. I was standing just off the third tee, behind the fairway ropes, watching my three favorite golfers in the world approach the tee box: Jack

① sanity ['sænɪti] n. 神志正常；心智健康；头脑清楚；通情达理

几年前我被诊断出癌症，这是我人生中最艰难的一段时期。我想，正是由于我的幽默感，才让我还能保持高度的理智。正如许多经历过化疗的人一样，我的头发都掉光了，看起来就像是一颗光亮的台球。我原本就十分喜爱戴帽子，所以当我全秃了以后，我就买了几顶自带头发的那种帽子。这样很方便，我也不用担心我的发型是否好看。

我是一个狂热的高尔夫球迷。事实上，我去过 23 场美国高尔夫公开赛的现场。有一次，在我的癌症治疗期间，我和丈夫约翰决定离开明尼苏达州的寒冷冬天，前往亚利桑那州的斯科茨代尔旅行。那儿正举行职业高球员协会（PGA）宿将巡回赛，这一传统赛事似乎让我的精神为之一振。

第一天的锦标赛仿佛上演在一个巨型画廊里，如此美丽，至若天堂。我站在第三个球座的旁边，前面就是球道绳索，能一眼看见我最喜欢的三个高尔夫球手：杰克·尼克劳斯、雷蒙德·弗洛伊德和汤姆·维斯科普夫在发球台上的飒爽英姿。

Nicklaus, Raymond Floyd and Tom Weiskopf.

Just as they arrived at the tee, the unimaginable happened. A huge gust of wind came up from out of nowhere and blew my hat and hair right off my head and into the middle of the fairway! The thousands of **spectators**[①] lining the fairway fell into an awkward silence, all eyes on me. Even my golf idols were watching me, as my hair was in their flight path. I was mortified! Embarrassed as I was, I knew I couldn't just stand there. Someone had to do something to get things moving again.

So I took a deep breath, went under the ropes and out into the middle of the fairway. I grabbed my hat and hair, nestled them back on my head as best I could. Then I turned to the golfers and loudly announced, "Gentlemen, the wind is blowing from left to right."

They said the laughter could be heard all the way to the nineteenth hole.

① spectator ['spɛkˌtetɚ] n. 观众，旁观者

正当他们走到球座旁时，意想不到的事情发生了。不知道从哪儿刮来一阵大风，将我配有头发的帽子吹到了赛道中央！万千的观众顿时鸦雀无声，气氛极为尴尬，我被各种眼光包围着。甚至连我的高尔夫偶像也盯着我看，因为我的帽子和头发占了他们的赛道。真苦恼！这情况尴尬至极，我知道我不能只呆站在那里，总得有谁来打破这个僵局。

于是，我深吸了一口气，沿着绳索往下走到了赛道中间。我抓起这顶带假发的帽子，尽可能优雅地将它重新戴回头顶。然后我转向了高尔夫球手们，向他们大声喊道："嘿，先生们，风向是从左往右的！"

据说，当时 1 到 19 号洞口的观众席都洋溢起欢乐的笑声。

My Father's Music
父亲的音乐

◎ Wayne Kalyn

I remember the day Dad first lugged the heavy accordion up our front stoop, taxing his small frame. He gathered my mother and me in the living room and opened the case as if it were a treasure chest. "Here it is," he said. "Once you learn to play, it'll stay with you for life."

If my thin smile didn't match his full-fledged grin, it was because I had prayed for a guitar or a piano. For the next two weeks, the accordion was stored in the hall closet. Then one evening Dad announced that I would start lessons the following week. In disbelief I shot my eyes toward Mom for support. The firm set of her jaw told me I was out of luck.

Spending $300 for an accordion and $5 per lesson was out of character for my father. He was practical always—something he learned growing up on a Pennsylvania farm. Clothes, heat and sometimes even food were scarce.

Dad was a **supervisor**① in a company that serviced jet engines. Weekends, he tinkered in the cellar, turning scraps of plywood into a utility cabinet or fixing

① supervisor ['sjupə,vaɪzə] n. 监督者，管理者；镇长

我还记得那一天——瘦弱的父亲将沉重的手风琴费力地拖到前门的情景。他招呼我和妈妈到客厅里来，然后打开了这个他视若珍宝的箱子。“看这个，”他说，“一旦你学会了它，它便会成为你终身的伙伴。”

和他发自内心的笑容不同，我只是勉强地笑了笑。因为我期待已久的，其实是一把吉他或一台钢琴。在接下来的两周里，那架手风琴都一直被放在走廊的壁橱里。一天傍晚，父亲突然宣布，我从下周起就要开始学手风琴了。带着疑惑，我赶忙向妈妈使眼色以求支援。可她紧绷的下巴告诉我，我不走运了。

花 300 美元买一架手风琴，每次上课再花 5 美元，这着实不符合父亲的性格。他一直是比较务实的——这是他在宾夕法尼亚州的农场习来的。衣物、暖气，甚至有时候连食物都会紧缺。

爸爸在一家为喷气式飞机提供引擎服务的公司担任主管。周末，他也总是在地下室里捣鼓，把一些胶合板的边角料做成实用的柜子，或者用一

a broken toy with spare parts. Quiet and shy, he was never more comfortable than when at his workbench.

Only music carried Dad away from his world of tools and projects. On a Sunday drive, he turned the radio on immediately. At red lights, I'd notice his foot tapping in time. He seemed to hang on every note.

Still, I wasn't prepared when, **rummaging**[1] in a closet, I found a case that looked to me like a tiny guitar's. Opening it, I saw the polished glow of a beautiful violin. "It's your father's," Mom said. "His parents bought it for him. I guess he got too busy on the farm to ever learn to play it." I tried to imagine Dad's rough hands on this delicate instrument—and couldn't.

I was ordered to practice half an hour every day, and every day I tried to get out of it. My future seemed to be outside playing ball, not in the house mastering songs I would soon forget. But my parents hounded me to practice.

Gradually, to my surprise, I was able to string notes together and coordinate my hands to play simple songs. Often, after supper, my father would request a tune or two. As he sat in his easy chair, I would fumble through "Lady of Spain" and "Beer Barrel Polka".

"Very nice, better than last week," he'd say. Then I would follow into a melody of his favorites, "Red River Valley" and "Home on the Range", and he would drift off to sleep, the newspaper folded on his lap. I took it as a compliment that he could relax under the spell of my playing.

One July evening I was giving an almost flawless rendition of "Come Back to Sorrento", and my parents called me to an open window. An elderly neighbor,

① rummage ['rʌmɪdʒ] v. 翻查；搜出；翻箱倒柜

些零件把坏了的玩具修好。他性格内向腼腆，没有什么地方比工作台更能让他感到舒适了。

只有音乐能让父亲走出他那满是工具和材料的世界。在一个周日，我们驾车外出的时候，他一上车就打开了收音机。遇到红灯时，我注意到他的脚在有节奏地打着拍子，貌似还挺合拍的。

然而，当我在壁橱里翻找出一个像是装小吉他的盒子时，还是挺意外的。打开一看，是一把锃亮而漂亮的小提琴。“这是你父亲的，”妈妈说，“你祖父母买给他的。我想他平时忙于农务，所以没有时间学。”我试着想象父亲那粗糙的手在这精致的乐器上拨弄的场景——简直无法想象。

爸爸要求我每天练琴半小时，但我每天都想躲开。我的未来应该是在户外打球，而不是在屋里重复着这些让我很快就会忘记的歌曲。但父母总是不断地敦促我练习。

令我惊喜的是，我渐渐能把几个零散的音符串联在一起，演奏出简单的歌曲了，手的协调性也好多了。晚饭后，父亲常常让我拉上一两首曲子。他躺在老爷椅里，听我笨拙地拉完《西班牙女郎》和《波尔卡啤酒桶》。

他会说：“非常好，比上周好多了。”然后我就继续拉他喜欢的曲子《红河谷》和《山上之家》，他会在我的歌声中慢慢入睡，报纸就叠在膝盖上。我把这看作一种赞扬：他能够在我的琴声中得到放松。

rarely seen outside her house, was leaning against our car humming dreamily to the tune. When I finished, she smiled broadly and called out, "I remember that song as a child in Italy. Beautiful, just beautiful."

Throughout the summer, Mr. Zelli's lessons grew more difficult. It took me a week and a half to master them now. All the while I could hear my buddies outside playing heated games of stickball. I'd also hear an occasional **taunt**①; "Hey, where's your monkey and cup?"

Such humiliation paled, though, beside the impending fall recital. I would have to play a solo on a local movie theater's stage. I wanted to skip the whole thing. Emotions boiled over in the car one Sunday afternoon. "I don't want to play a solo." I said. "You have to," replied my father.

"Why?" I shouted. "Because you didn't get to play your violin when you were a kid? Why should I have to play this stupid instrument when you never had to play yours?" Dad pulled the car over and pointed at me. "Because you can bring people joy. You can touch their hearts. That's a gift I won't let you throw away." He added softly, "Someday you'll have the chance I never had: you'll play beautiful music for your family. And you'll understand why you've worked so hard."

I was speechless. I had rarely heard Dad speak with such feeling about anything, much less the accordion. From then on, I practiced without my parents' making me.

The evening of the concert Mom wore glittery earrings and more makeup than I could remember. Dad got out of work early, put on a suit and tie, and

① taunt [tɔnt] n. 嘲弄，奚落；讥讽；嘲弄的对象，笑柄

7月的一个傍晚，我正在拉《重返索伦托》，效果近乎完美。父母突然把我叫到窗前。一位不太出门、上了年纪的邻居正靠在我们的车上，沉醉地跟着调子哼唱。曲终，她欣喜地笑了，大声说道："我小时候在意大利就听过这首歌。美，真是太美了！"

整个夏天，泽利先生的课变得越来越难。我现在得花上一周半的时间才能掌握。我总是听到伙伴们在室外玩棍子球的欢闹声。偶尔还会听到一声讽刺："嘿，伙计，你的猴子和奖杯哪儿去了？"

不过，这种羞辱与即将到来的秋季演奏会相比，就显得微不足道了。我会在当地一家影院的舞台上独奏一曲。我很想躲过这一切。一个周日的下午，我的情绪在车上爆发了。"我真的不想独奏。"我抱怨道。"你必须这样做。"父亲只回了我这几个字。

"为什么？"我吼道，"难道就因为你小时候没能拉小提琴吗？你都从来不拉琴，为什么我就一定得拉这笨重的乐器？"父亲将车停在路边，指着我说，"因为你能给人们带来欢乐。你能触动他们的心弦。我不能让你丢掉这种天赋。"他语气稍缓，"某一天你会拥有我从不曾拥有的机会：你能为你的家人演奏美妙的音乐。那时你就能明白自己如此努力的原因了。"

我顿时语塞。我极少能感受到父亲掏心窝的话，更别说是因为拉手风琴的事了。从那时起，即使父母不敦促，我也会自觉地练琴。

slicked down his hair with Vitalis. They were ready an hour early, so we sat in the living room chatting nervously. I got the unspoken message that playing this one song was a dream come true for them.

音乐会那晚，我记得母亲戴上了闪亮的耳环，精心打扮了一番。父亲也早早下了班，西装革履，还用乳液将头发抹得油亮亮的。他们提前一个小时就准备好了，我们坐在客厅紧张地聊着。我能感觉到，我演奏这首歌曲，就是实现了他们的一个梦想。

A Service of Love (Ⅰ)
爱的奉献（1）

◎ O. Henry

When one loves one's Art no service seems too hard.

That is our premise. This story shall draw a conclusion from it, and show at the same time that the premise is incorrect. That will be a new thing in logic, and a feat in story-telling somewhat older than the Great Wall of China.

Joe Larrabee came out of the post-oak flats of the Middle West pulsing with a genius for pictorial art. At six he drew a picture of the town pump with a prominent citizen passing it hastily. This effort was framed and hung in the drug store window by the side of the ear of corn with an uneven number of rows. At twenty he left for New York with a flowing necktie and a capital tied up somewhat closer.

Delia Caruthers did things in six octaves so promisingly in a pine-tree village in the South that her relatives chipped in enough in her chip hat for her to go "North" and "finish". They could not see her f—, but that is our story.

Joe and Delia met in an atelier where a number of art and music students had gathered to discuss chiaroscuro, Wagner, music, Rembrandt's works,

一旦某个人爱上了另一个人的艺术，那么一切奉献都不在话下。

那是我们的前提。这个故事将由此得出结论，同时表明这个前提是错的。这从逻辑上讲要数新鲜的事了，可从讲故事的技艺上看，却已像中国的万里长城那般古老。

乔·拉腊比来自美国中西部的栎树平原，他整个人的骨子里都脉动着绘画的天赋。6 岁时他画了一幅画，画中是一台镇上的抽水机，画面显现出一位匆匆路过的行人。这幅作品被装上框挂在药店的橱窗上，画旁是几排数目不等的玉米穗。20 岁时，他前往纽约，当时的他领带飘摇，钱包更是飘渺。

来自南方松树村庄的迪莉娅·凯鲁瑟斯能将六个八度弹得出神入化，于是她的亲朋好友们凑份子让她去“北方”“深造”。他们无法预知她的未来——，而这就是我们要讲的故事。

乔和迪莉娅在一个画室里邂逅对方，一些学艺术和音乐的学生聚集在这画室里讨论明暗效果、瓦格纳、音乐、伦布兰特的作品、绘画、瓦尔特

pictures, Waldteufel, wall paper, Chopin and Oolong.

Joe and Delia became enamored one of the other, or each of the other, as you please, and in a short time were married—for (see above), when one loves one's Art no service seems too hard.

Mr. and Mrs. Larrabee began housekeeping in a flat. It was a lonesome flat—something like the A sharp way down at the left-hand end of the keyboard. And they were happy; for they had their Art, and they had each other. And my advice to the rich young man would be—sell all thou hast, and give it to the poor—janitor for the privilege of living in a flat with your Art and your Delia.

Flat-dwellers shall indorse my dictum that theirs is the only true happiness. If a home is happy it cannot fit too close—let the dresser collapse and become a billiard table; let the mantel turn to a rowing machine, the escritoire to a spare bedchamber, the washstand to an upright piano; let the four walls come together, if they will, so you and your Delia are between. But if home be the other kind, let it be wide and long—enter you at the Golden Gate, hang your hat on Hatteras, your cape on Cape Horn and go out by the Labrador.

Joe was painting in the class of the great Magister—you know his fame. His fees are high; his lessons are light—his high-lights have brought him renown. Delia was studying under Rosenstock—you know his repute as a disturber of the piano keys.

They were mighty happy as long as their money lasted. So is every—but I will not be cynical. Their aims were very clear and defined. Joe was to become capable very soon of turning out pictures that old gentlemen with thin side-whiskers and thick pocketbooks would sandbag one another in his studio for the

费尔、壁纸、肖邦和奥朗。

乔和迪莉娅一见倾心，或是相互倾心，你高兴怎么说就怎么说，而且不久就结为了夫妻——因为（见上文），一旦某个人爱上了另一个人的艺术，那么一切奉献都不在话下。

从此以后，拉腊比夫妇就在一所公寓里过起了日子。公寓非常冷清——就像左手末端琴键上的A音一样陡然滑落。他们生活得很幸福；因为他们拥有自己的艺术，还拥有彼此。我要劝那些有钱的年轻人，卖掉你的家当，然后将卖得的钱交给穷苦的守门人吧——以争取和你的艺术以及迪莉娅一起在公寓里生活的权利。

居住在公寓里的人们会认可我的说法，那就是，他们拥有的幸福才是唯一真实的幸福。幸福的家庭拥挤得只能一物多用又何妨——让壁橱翻倒充当台球桌，将壁炉架当作划船器，将写字桌当作临时的卧榻，洗脸架充当竖式钢琴；如果可能的话，让四堵墙壁挤拢来，将你和你的迪莉娅围在中间。但倘若是另一类的家庭，也就无所谓它是多么宽大——你可以从金门海峡进门，将帽子挂在哈特勒斯，将披肩挂在合恩角，出门还要经过拉布拉多。

乔在著名的曼切斯特老师那儿学画——你也知道他的名声。他收费高昂，课程轻松——他也因此而闻名。迪莉娅在罗森斯托克那儿学习——你也知道他是一个出了名的专跟钢琴键过不去的家伙。

只要他们的钱还没用完，生活就很幸福。每个家庭都是这样——可我并不悲观。他们的目标非常清晰明确。乔很快就能作出一些画作，那些鬓须稀疏而钱袋殷实的老先生们，就会挤满他的画室，争相购买他的作品。

privilege of buying. Delia was to become familiar and then contemptuous with Music, so that when she saw the orchestra seats and boxes unsold she could have sore throat and lobster in a private dining-room and refuse to go on the stage.

But the best, in my opinion, was the home life in the little flat—the ardent, voluble chats after the day's study; the cozy dinners and fresh, light breakfasts; the interchange of ambitions—ambitions interwoven each with the other's or else inconsiderable—the mutual help and inspiration; and—overlook my artlessness—stuffed olives and cheese sandwiches at 11 p.m.

But after a while Art flagged. It sometimes does, even if some switchman doesn't flag it. Everything going out and nothing coming in, as the vulgarians say. Money was lacking to pay Mr. Magister and Herr Rosenstock their prices. When one loves one's Art no service seems too hard. So, Delia said she must give music lessons to keep the chafing dish bubbling.

For two or three days she went out canvassing for pupils. One evening she came home elated.

"Joe, dear," she said, gleefully, "I've a pupil. And, oh, the loveliest people! General—General A. B. Pinkney's daughter—on Seventy-first street. Such a splendid house, Joe—you ought to see the front door! Byzantine I think you would call it. And inside! Oh, Joe, I never saw anything like it before.

"My pupil is his daughter Clementina. I dearly love her already. She's a delicate thing-dresses always in white; and the sweetest, simplest manners! Only eighteen years old. I'm to give three lessons a week; and, just think, Joe! $5 a lesson. I don't mind it a bit; for when I get two or three more pupils I can resume my lessons with Herr Rosenstock. Now, smooth out that wrinkle between your

迪莉娅要把音乐练熟，达到对其不屑一顾的程度，以至于要是她见到音乐厅里的位置和包厢不满座，她就可以谎称喉咙痛，在专用的餐室里吃龙虾，拒绝登台。

可在我看来，最美满的还是小公寓里的家庭生活：一天的学习之后，夫妻俩热情地促膝交谈；享受舒适的晚饭和清新淡雅的早餐；互诉心中的梦想——与对方有关的梦想，否则就不予考虑——相互帮助与启发；还有，恕我不懂讲究——晚上 11 点钟饱吃一顿橄榄和奶酪三明治。

可是没过多久，艺术就偃旗息鼓。即使没有人去动摇它，有时它自己也会衰落。俗话说，坐吃山空，他们的钱已经不够交曼切斯特和罗森斯托克两位先生的学费了。一旦某个人爱上了另一个人的艺术，那么一切奉献都不在话下。于是迪莉娅说，她要去教音乐，以维持三餐供应。

她在外面奔走了两三天，兜揽学生。一天晚上，她兴高采烈地回到家。

“乔，亲爱的，”她高兴地说，“我招到了一个学生。而且，哦，那家人可爱极了！她是住在 71 号街的一位将军——埃·皮·品克奈将军的女儿。他们家的房子非常华丽，乔——你真该去看看那大门！我想你会说那是拜占庭风格。还有里面！哦，乔，我从没有见过那样的房子。

“我收的学生就是他的女儿克莱门蒂娜。我可喜欢她了。她是个娇美的小家伙，总是穿白色的衣服；而且她举止可爱又淳朴！她只有 18 岁。我每星期上三次课；你想想看，乔！每节课 5 块钱。可是我一点也不在乎；等我再找到两三个学生，我又可以到罗森斯托克先生那儿去学习了。所以，别皱眉了，亲爱的，让我们好好享受一顿晚餐吧。”

brows, dear, and let's have a nice supper."

"That's all right for you, Dele," said Joe, attacking a can of peas with a carving knife and a hatchet, "but how about me? Do you think I'm going to let you hustle for wages while I philander in the regions of high art? Not by the bones of Benvenuto Cellini! I guess I can sell papers or lay cobblestones, and bring in a dollar or two."

Delia came and hung about his neck.

"Joe, dear, you are silly. You must keep on at your studies. It is not as if I had quit my music and gone to work at something else. While I teach I learn. I am always with my music. And we can live as happily as millionaires on $15 a week. You mustn't think of leaving Mr. Magister."

"All right," said Joe, reaching for the blue scalloped vegetable dish. "But I hate for you to be giving lessons. It isn't Art. But you're a trump and a dear to do it."

"When one loves one's Art no service seems too hard," said Delia.

"Magister praised the sky in that sketch I made in the park," said Joe. "And Tinkle gave me permission to hang two of them in his window. I may sell one if the right kind of a moneyed idiot sees them."

"I'm sure you will," said Delia, sweetly. "And now let's be thankful for Gen. Pinkney and this veal roast."

“你倒好了，迪莉，”乔说着，用小斧和餐刀撬开一听青豆，“可我怎么办呢？你以为我能让你忙着挣钱，而自己却徜徉在崇高的艺术中吗？我以本韦努托·切利尼的尸骨赌咒，绝对不能！我想我可以卖卖报纸，或去搬石头铺马路，这样多少也能挣得一两美元。”

迪莉娅走过来，环住他的脖子。

“乔，你真傻。你一定要坚持作画。我并没有放弃音乐去做其他的事啊。我边教书也边学习呢。我一直与我的音乐同在。即便每周只赚 15 美元，我们也可以像百万富翁那样幸福地生活。你可千万别想离开曼切斯特先生的课堂。”

“没错，”乔说着伸手去拿那只荷叶花边的蓝色盘子，“可是我不想让你去教课。那可不是艺术。你真好，竟愿意做这般牺牲。”

“一旦某个人爱上了另一个人的艺术，那么一切奉献都不在话下。”迪莉娅说。

“曼切斯特夸奖了我在公园里画的那幅素描，他说上面的天空画得很不错，”乔说，“丁克还答应让我在他的橱窗里挂上两幅。若是哪个有钱的傻瓜看中了它，我还可以卖出一幅。”

“我相信你一定能卖出去，”迪莉娅甜蜜地说，“现在，还是让我们感谢品克奈将军和这些烤肉吧。”

A Service of Love (Ⅱ)
爱的奉献（2）

◎ O. Henry

During all of the next week the Larrabees had an early breakfast. Joe was enthusiastic about some morning-effect sketches he was doing in Central Park, and Delia packed him off breakfasted, coddled, praised and kissed at 7 o'clock. Art is an engaging mistress. It was most times 7 o'clock when he returned in the evening.

At the end of the week Delia, sweetly proud but languid, triumphantly tossed three five-dollar bills on the 8x10 (inches) centre table of the 8x10 (feet) flat parlour.

"Sometimes," she said, a little wearily, "Clementina tries me. I'm afraid she doesn't practice enough, and I have to tell her the same things so often. And then she always dresses entirely in white, and that does get monotonous. But Gen. Pinkney is the dearest old man! I wish you could know him, Joe. He comes in sometimes when I am with Clementina at the piano—he is a widower, you know—and stands there pulling his white goatee. 'And how are the semiquavers and the demisemiquavers progressing?' he always asks.

"I wish you could see the wainscoting in that drawing-room, Joe! And those

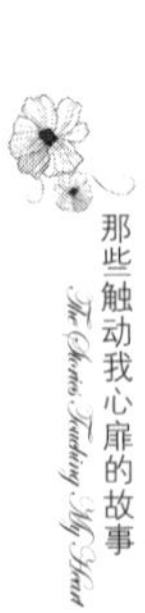

接下来的一整个星期，拉腊比夫妇早早就吃过了早餐。乔兴致满满地来到中央公园画他的晨间印象素描，七点时分，迪莉娅为他送来早饭，顺道向他撒撒娇，赞美一番他的画作，两人再亲吻一阵。艺术是一位迷人的情妇。他晚上回家时，大多已是 7 点钟了。

到了周末，骄傲中带着疲倦的迪莉娅就会得意洋洋地将三张 5 美元钞票扔在 80×10（英尺）的客厅中间那张 80×10（英寸）的桌子上。

“有时候，”她略显疲倦地说，“克里门蒂娜可让人费劲了。恐怕她根本没练习到位，同样的问题我要重复好多遍。而且她全身都穿成白色，看上去既单调又乏味。可品克奈将军却好得没话说！我希望你能够认识他，乔。有时他会在我与克里门蒂娜弹钢琴时进来——他是个鳏夫，你知道的——他就站在那儿，捋着他白色的山羊胡子。‘16 分音符和 32 分音符学得怎么样了？’他总是问。”

“我希望你能看看那客厅里的壁板，乔！还有那些阿斯特拉罕的毯式门帷。克里门蒂娜总有些微微咳嗽。我希望她的身体不像看起来那么娇弱。

Astrakhan rug portieres. And Clementina has such a funny little cough. I hope she is stronger than she looks. Oh, I really am getting attached to her, she is so gentle and high bred. Gen. Pinkney's brother was once Minister to Bolivia."

And then Joe, with the air of a Monte Cristo, drew forth a ten, a five, a two and a one—all legal tender notes—and laid them beside Delia's earnings.

"Sold that watercolor of the obelisk to a man from Peoria," he announced overwhelmingly.

"Don't joke with me," said Delia, "not from Peoria!"

"All the way. I wish you could see him, Dele. Fat man with a woollen muffler and a quill toothpick. He saw the sketch in Tinkle's window and thought it was a windmill at first, he was game, though, and bought it anyhow. He ordered another—an oil sketch of the Lackawanna freight depot—to take back with him. Music lessons! Oh, I guess Art is still in it."

"I'm so glad you've kept on," said Delia, heartily. "You're bound to win, dear. Thirty-three dollars! We never had so much to spend before. We'll have oysters to-night."

"And filet mignon with champignons," said Joe. "Were is the olive fork?"

On the next Saturday evening Joe reached home first. He spread his $18 on the parlour table and washed what seemed to be a great deal of dark paint from his hands.

Half an hour later Delia arrived, her right hand tied up in a shapeless bundle of wraps and bandages.

"How is this?" asked Joe after the usual greetings. Delia laughed, but not very joyously.

喔，我真是越来越喜欢她了，她这么温柔，又有教养。品克奈将军的弟弟还曾担任过驻波利维亚公使。”

接着，乔带着基督山伯爵的神气，掏出一张 10 元、一张 5 元、一张 2 元和一张 1 元的钞票——全是合法的纸币——放在迪莉娅的钱旁边。

“那幅方尖石塔水彩画卖给了一个从皮奥里亚来的男人，”他郑重其事地宣布。

“别跟我开玩笑啦，”迪莉娅说，“不是从皮奥里亚来的吧！”

“就是那儿来的。我希望你能见见他，迪莉。他胖胖的，围着羊毛围巾，还咬着羽毛牙签。他在丁克的橱窗里看到了那幅画，刚开始还以为是风车呢。他倒很气派，一口气就买下了。他还预定了一幅拉克万纳货站的油画——准备带回去。我的音乐课！呵，我想艺术还是有用的。”

“我很高兴你坚持下来了，”迪莉娅由衷地说，“你注定会成功的，亲爱的。33 美元啊！我们之前可从没有过这么多钱。我们今晚可以吃牡蛎咯。”

“再来点菲力牛排加金针菇，”乔说，“橄榄叉在哪儿？”

接下来的那个周六晚上，乔先回到家。他把他的 18 块钱摊在客厅的桌子上，然后把手上大块貌似黑色颜料的东西洗干净。

半个钟头以后，迪莉娅来了，她的右手用绷带胡乱地缠成一团。

“怎么回事？”乔照例问候之后问道。迪莉娅笑了，可是笑得并不十分欢乐。

“克里门蒂娜，”她解释说，“上了课之后一定要吃奶酪面包。她真是个

"Clementina," she explained, "insisted upon a Welsh rabbit after her lesson. She is such a queer girl. Welsh rabbits at 5 in the afternoon. The General was there. You should have seen him run for the chafing dish, Joe, just as if there wasn't a servant in the house. I know Clementina isn't in good health; she is so nervous. In serving the rabbit she spilled a great lot of it, boiling hot, over my hand and wrist. It hurt awfully, Joe. And the dear girl was so sorry! But Gen. Pinkney!—Joe, that old man nearly went distracted. He rushed downstairs and sent somebody—they said the furnace man or somebody in the basement—out to a drug store for some oil and things to bind it up with. It doesn't hurt so much now."

"What's this?" asked Joe, taking the hand tenderly and pulling at some white strands beneath the bandages.

"It's something soft," said Delia, "that had oil on it. Oh, Joe, did you sell another sketch?" She had seen the money on the table.

"Did I?" said Joe; "just ask the man from Peoria. He got his depot to-day, and he isn't sure but he thinks he wants another parkscape and a view on the Hudson. What time this afternoon did you burn your hand, Dele?"

"Five o'clock, I think," said Dele, plaintively. "The iron—I mean the rabbit came off the fire about that time. You ought to have seen Gen. Pinkney, Joe, when—"

"Sit down here a moment, Dele," said Joe. He drew her to the couch, sat beside her and put his arm across her shoulders.

"What have you been doing for the last two weeks, Dele?" he asked.

She braved it for a moment or two with an eye full of love and stubbornness,

古怪的女孩儿，下午5点钟还要吃威尔士干酪。将军也在场。你该看看他奔去拿烘锅的样子，乔，好像家里没有佣人似的，我知道克里门蒂娜身体不好；她神经脆弱。她浇奶酪时泼翻了许多，滚烫的，溅在我的手腕上。痛得要命，乔。那可爱的女孩难过极了！还有品克奈将军！乔，那老头儿差点要发狂了。他冲下楼去叫人，他们说是烧炉子的或是地下室里的什么人，到药房里去买了一些油和别的东西来替我包扎。现在倒不怎么痛了。"

"这是什么？"乔轻轻地握住那只手，扯着绷带下面的几根白线，问道。

"那是软纱，"迪莉娅说，"上面涂了油。喔，乔，你又卖了画吗？"她看到了桌子上的钱。

"有吗？"乔说，"只是去问了问那个从皮奥里亚来的人。他今天来取了画，他还没怎么确定，可能还要一幅公园景致和一幅哈得逊河风景。你今天下午什么时候烫到手的，迪莉娅？"

"大概5点钟吧，"迪莉娅可怜巴巴地说，"那个熨——我是说奶酪，大概在那个时候烧好。你真该看到品克奈将军，乔，他……"

"先在这儿坐一会儿吧，迪莉，"乔说着扶她到沙发上，坐在她身旁，用手臂圈住她的肩膀。

"这两个星期来，你到底在做什么呀，迪莉？"他问道。

她定了一会儿神，眼神里充满了爱意和倔强，之后小声嘟哝了几句，提到了品克奈将军；可最终垂下头来，一边哭，一边说了实话。

and murmured a phrase or two vaguely of Gen. Pinkney; but at length down went her head and out came the truth and tears.

"I couldn't get any pupils," she confessed. "And I couldn't bear to have you give up your lessons; and I got a place ironing shirts in that big Twenty-fourth street laundry. And I think I did very well to make up both General Pinkney and Clementina, don't you, Joe? And when a girl in the laundry set down a hot iron on my hand this afternoon I was all the way home making up that story about the Welsh rabbit. You're not angry, are you, Joe? And if I hadn't got the work you mightn't have sold your sketches to that man from Peoria."

"He wasn't from Peoria," said Joe, slowly.

"Well, it doesn't matter where he was from. How clever you are, Joe—and—kiss me, Joe—and what made you ever suspect that I wasn't giving music lessons to Clementina?"

"I didn't," said Joe, "until to-night. And I wouldn't have then, only I sent up this cotton waste and oil from the engine-room this afternoon for a girl upstairs who had her hand burned with a smoothing-iron. I've been firing the engine in that laundry for the last two weeks."

"And then you didn't—"

"My purchaser from Peoria," said Joe, "and Gen. Pinkney are both creations of the same art—but you wouldn't call it either painting or music."

And then they both laughed, and Joe began:

"When one loves one's Art no service seems—"

But Delia stopped him with her hand on his lips. "No," she said—"just 'When one loves'."

“我找不到学生，”她供认道，“我又不忍心看你放弃你的课程，于是在24号街那家大洗衣作坊里找了份烫衬衣的活儿。我以为我把品克奈将军和克里门蒂娜两个人编造得很好呢，可不是吗，乔？今天下午，洗衣坊里一个姑娘的热熨斗烫了我的手，我一路上就编出那个威尔士干酪的故事。你不会生我的气，对吧，乔？如果我不去做工，你也许不可能把你的画卖给那个皮奥里亚人。”

“他不是从皮奥利亚来的。”乔慢慢吞吞地说。

“他打哪儿来都一样。你真聪明，乔——亲亲我，乔——你怎么会怀疑我没有教克里门蒂娜音乐呢？”

“我没有，”乔说，“直到今晚前都没有怀疑，本来今晚也不会起疑的，可是今天下午，我把机器间的油和废纱头送给楼上一个被熨斗烫了手的姑娘。两星期来，我就在那家洗衣作坊的炉子房烧火。”

“那你并没有——”

“我那位皮奥里亚来的买主，”乔说，“和品克奈将军都是同一艺术的产物——只是那既非绘画也非音乐罢了。”

接着，两人都笑了，乔说：

“当一个人爱上了另一个人的艺术，那么一切奉献都——”

可是迪莉娅用手掩住了他的嘴。“不，”她说——“只需说‘当一个人爱上了另一个人’。”

Swans Mate for Life

天鹅的爱情

◎ Hal Torrance

The end of my sophomore year was approaching. Mom called me at the dorm one **muggy**[①] evening during the last week of May. My summer break would be spent with Grandma and Grandpa, helping out around their farm. The arrangement made good sense to all the family. I wasn't fully convinced of that myself but figured it was just one summer. Next year would be my little brother's turn.

I packed my car after my last exam and said my good-byes until the fall. My friends would keep until then. Most of them were going home for the summer anyway.

The farm was about a three-hour drive from school. My grandparents were both in their seventies, and I knew they really needed the help around the farm. Getting in the hay would be something Grandpa couldn't do by himself. He also needed help with repairs to the barns and a host of other chores.

I arrived late that afternoon. Grandma had fixed more food than the three

① muggy ['mʌgi] a. 闷热的

我大学的第二个学年即将结束。5 月最后一个礼拜，一个闷热的夜晚，母亲打电话到宿舍告诉我说，今年夏天我将要和爷爷奶奶共度暑假，去他们的农场上帮忙。这个安排对全家人都有好处，我却并不十分信服，不过转念一想，也只是一个暑假罢了。明年就该轮到我弟弟了。

最后一场考试结束后，我就整理好了行装放进车里，并与我的朋友们告别，相约秋天再见。他们大多数人都会回家过暑假。

农场离学校有三个小时的车程。我的爷爷奶奶都是年届七旬的老人，他们的确需要帮手来帮忙打理农场。爷爷独自一人没法收割干草，而且他也需要有人帮忙修理谷仓，做其他的一些杂务。

那天下午晚些时候，我到达了农场。奶奶准备了很多食物，我们三个人根本都吃不完。她太宠爱我了，我原以为一旦她习惯了我在身边，对我的关注就会慢慢消退，但是，后来的事实证明并非如此。爷爷几乎做得面

of us could possibly eat. She **doted**[1] over me entirely too much. I figured all the attention would taper off once she got used to having me around, but it didn't. Grandpa wanted to bring me up to date on literally everything. By the time I settled in for bed that night, I'd decided things would be okay. After all, it was just for one summer.

The next morning, Grandpa fixed breakfast for the two of us. He told me Grandma had tired herself out yesterday and was going to rest in bed a little longer. I made a mental note to myself to not ask her to do things for me while I was there. I was there to help, not be a burden.

Grandpa surprised me that morning. Once we were out of the house, he seemed more in his own element. The farm was his domain. Despite his age, there was confidence in the way he moved about the place. He didn't seem like the same person who had fallen asleep last night on the couch before the six o'clock news was finished. As we walked the pastures getting a close-up look at the livestock, Grandpa seemed to know each cow. And there were nearly two hundred of them!

We didn't do much real work that first day, but I gained a sense of appreciation for what Grandpa had done all those years before I was even born. He wasn't an educated man, but he had raised and provided for four children on this farm. I was impressed by that.

Weeks passed. By June we had already baled one cutting of hay and gotten it safely into the barn. I gradually settled into a routine of daily work with Grandpa. He had a mental schedule of things that needed doing, and we worked on part

---

① dote [dəut] v. 溺爱

面俱到，他想让我熟悉每一件事情。到晚上上床睡觉的时候，我告诉自己：没关系，一切都会好的。毕竟，我只待一个暑假而已。

第二天一早，爷爷为我们俩做好了早餐。他告诉我说奶奶昨天太累了，要在床上多休息一会儿。我在心里暗暗记下：以后不要让奶奶为我做事了，毕竟我是来这里帮忙的，我可不想成为他们的负担。

那天早晨，爷爷着实让人大吃一惊。我们一走出房子，爷爷似乎就立刻变得轻松自在起来。这座农场就是他的领地，尽管他年事已高，但他在这里四处走动的时候，总是显得自信满满，自得其乐。与昨晚 6 点新闻结束之前就在沙发上呼呼大睡的爷爷相比，现在的他似乎摇身一变，成了一个截然不同的人。我们走到草场上仔细查看牲畜，而爷爷似乎认识每一头牛，那里竟然有近两百头牛！

第一天，我们没干什么实质性的活儿，但对于爷爷从我出生前以来这些年一直从事的事情，我不禁从心底油然而生一股欣赏钦佩之情。他没受过什么教育，也没多少文化，但他却在这个农场上将四个子女抚养成人。我被深深地感动了。

一转眼，几个星期过去了。到 6 月的时候，我们已经将干草收割打捆，并顺利地送入谷仓。我逐渐适应了和爷爷一起完成每天的例行工作。对于需要做的事情，他脑子里列了一个时间表，每天我们都会各自完成这些工

of it each day. In the evenings I usually read or talked with Grandma. She never grew tired of hearing about college or anything I was involved in. She told me stories about her childhood, family and the early years after she and Grandpa had married.

The last Saturday in June, Grandpa suggested we go fishing, since we were caught up on everything. The pond was in a low pasture near the woods. Years before, Grandpa had stocked it with fish. We drove the pickup to the pond that day, looking over the livestock as we went. We hadn't expected what we saw when we got to the pond that morning: One of the swans was dead. Grandpa had given the pair of swans to Grandma on their fiftieth anniversary.

"Why don't we see about buying another one," I suggested, hoping the situation could somehow be righted. Grandpa thought for a few moments before answering. He finally said, "No...it's not that easy, Bruce. You see, swans mate for life." He raised his finger to point, holding the fishing pole in his other hand. "There's nothing we can do for the one that's left. He has to work it out for himself."

We caught enough fish that morning for lunch. On the way back to the house, Grandpa asked me not to tell Grandma about the swan. She didn't get down to the pond much anymore, and there was no sense in her knowing about it right away.

A few days later, we drove by the pond while doing our morning check on the cows. We found the other swan lying near the same spot we had found the first one. It, too, was dead.

The month of July started with me and Grandpa putting up a new stretch of

作。晚上，我时常和奶奶一块儿聊天或看书。她从来不会厌倦谈论我的大学生活以及与我有关的一切；而她也对我回忆起她的童年，她的家人，以及她和爷爷刚结婚那几年的往事。

6 月的最后一个星期六，爷爷提议我们去钓鱼，因为我们已经干完了所有当时能做的农活。池塘位于树林附近的一片低矮的草场中，几年前，爷爷在池塘里放养了很多鱼。那天，我们开着皮卡车去池塘边，途中还去查看了一下牲畜。当我们到达池塘的时候，看到了未曾预料到的意外一幕：一对天鹅中的一只死掉了。那对天鹅可是爷爷在结婚 50 周年纪念日送给奶奶的礼物。

"为什么我们不再买一只天鹅呢？"我提了个建议，想缓和一下当时的气氛。爷爷陷入了沉思，久久不回答我的问题。最后，他说道："不……没那么简单，孩子。天鹅一生只有一个伴侣。"他举起一根手指，另一只手上握着钓鱼竿，"我们不能为剩下的那只天鹅做什么，它要靠自己度过这个难关。"

那天上午，我们很快便钓到了很多鱼，足够午饭时美餐一顿了。在回家的路上，爷爷嘱咐我不要对奶奶提起天鹅的事。她现在很少去塘边，而且让她知道这件事也没有任何意义。

几天后的一个早晨，我们和往常一样开车去检查牲畜。路过池塘时，在那只天鹅死去的同一地点，我们发现那儿躺着另一只天鹅，它也已经死去了。

7 月初，我和爷爷开始建造一段新的围栏。然后，就到了 7 月 12 日——奶奶去世的那一天。那天早晨，我睡过头了，爷爷也没有来敲门。

fence. Then July 12 came. That was the day Grandma passed away. I'd overslept that morning. Grandpa had not knocked on my door, either. It was nearly eight o'clock by the time I could hurriedly dress myself and get down to the kitchen. I saw Dr. Morgan sitting at the kitchen table. He was a neighbor my grandparents' age, long since retired. He'd come to the house several times before on social calls. I immediately knew something was wrong. This morning, his tattered old black bag was by his feet, and my grandfather was obviously shaken.

Grandma had died suddenly that morning of a **stroke**[①]. By the afternoon, my parents were there. The old house was soon crowded with relatives and Grandpa's friends.

The funeral was held the next day. Grandpa had insisted on having it as soon as possible. On the second day after the funeral, Grandpa announced at the breakfast table, "This is a working farm. We have a lot of things to do. The rest of you should get back to your own lives." Most of the family had already left, but this was Grandpa's way of telling the rest it was time for them to go home. My parents were the last to leave after lunch.

Grandpa was not a man who could outwardly express his grief around others, and we all worried about him. There had been talk of his giving up the farm. My parents thought he was too old to live out there alone. He wouldn't hear of it, though. I was proud of the way the old man had stood his ground.

The rest of the summer flowed by. We stayed busy working. I thought there was something different about Grandpa but couldn't quite put my finger on it. I started to wonder if he would be better off living with someone after all, but I

① stroke [strəuk] n. 中风；击打；意外的运气

等我急匆匆穿好衣服，走下楼梯进入厨房的时候，都快到 8 点了。我看见摩根医生坐在餐桌边。他和我的爷爷奶奶年纪相仿，是他们的邻居，已经退休很多年了，以前也曾应邀来过好几次。我立刻发觉有什么事情发生了。这天早上，他那破旧的黑包就扔在脚边，而我爷爷明显有些摇晃，似乎站立不稳。

那天早晨，奶奶因为中风突然去世。到下午的时候，我父母也赶到了。这座老房子里很快挤满了亲戚和爷爷的朋友。

因为爷爷坚持让奶奶尽早入土为安，所以葬礼就在第二天举行。葬礼过后的第二天，爷爷在早餐时向大家宣布："这个农场还需要正常运作，我们有很多事情要做。其余的人都回到你们自己的生活中去吧。"大多数家人已经离开，但是爷爷要以自己的方式告诉留下的人，是时候该回去了。我父母是最迟离开的，那天午饭后他们也走了。

爷爷不是一个会在人前表达悲痛的人，我们都为他感到担忧。于是，有人提出让他放弃继续在农场生活。我父母也觉得他年纪太大，不适合独自在那里生活。但他并不听从他们的建议。老人以自己的方式坚守着自己的立场，我为他感到骄傲。

剩下的日子飞一般地过去。我们总是忙着干活。我觉察到爷爷有些变化，但我又不能明确说出有什么不同来。我开始想，如果他能和谁一起住，是否会对他更好一些。但是，我清楚地知道，他不能离开农场。

knew he could not leave the farm.

September was nearing, and part of me did not want to leave. I thought of skipping the fall semester and staying around a few more months. When I mentioned it, Grandpa quickly told me that my place was back at college.

The day finally came for me to pack my car and leave. I shook his hand and chanced a hug. As I drove down the driveway, I saw him in the rearview mirror. He waved to me and then walked to the pasture gate to start the morning livestock check. That's how I like to remember him.

Mom called me at school on a **blustery**[①] October day to tell me Grandpa had died. A neighbor had stopped by that morning for coffee and found him in the kitchen. He died of a stroke, same as Grandma. At that moment, I understood what he'd clumsily tried to explain to me about the swan on that morning we fished together by the pond.

① blustery ['blʌstəri] a. 大风的；猛烈的；狂暴的

9 月渐渐临近，我有些不愿意离去。我甚至想过秋天的那个学期不去上学，而在农场上多待几个月时间。当我跟爷爷说起我的想法时，他毅然告诉我说，学校才是我该去的地方。

离开的那一天最终还是来临了，我不得不打点行装，回到学校去。我握了握他的手，同他拥抱了一下。我一边驾车沿着公路向前开去，一边在后视镜里看着他。他冲我挥挥手，然后走向草场门口，开始每天早晨检查牲口的工作。我喜欢以这种方式来记住他。

10 月的一天，寒风凛冽，妈妈打电话来学校告诉我，爷爷去世了。他的一个邻居早上过去喝咖啡时，在厨房里发现了他。他和奶奶一样死于中风。就在那时，我忽然明白，我们一起在池塘边钓鱼的那个早晨，他为什么笨拙地试图向我解释天鹅的故事。

A Story Happened on an Island
孤岛上的故事

◎ Anonymous

The only survivor of a shipwreck was washed up on a small, **uninhabited**[1] island. He prayed feverishly for God to rescue him, and every day he scanned the horizon for help, but none seemed forthcoming.

Exhausted, he eventually managed to build a little hut out of driftwood to protect him from the elements, and to store his few possessions. But then one day, after **scavenging**[2] for food, he arrived home to find his little hut in flames, the smoke rolling up to the sky.

The worst had happened; everything was lost.

He was stunned with grief and anger. "God how you could do this to me!" he cried.

Early the next day, however, he was awakened by the sound of a ship that was approaching the island. It had come to rescue him. "How did you know I was here?" asked the weary man of his rescuers. "We saw your smoke signal,"

① uninhabited [ˌʌnɪn'hæbɪtɪd] a. 无人居住的，无人烟的，荒凉的；杳无人烟的
② scavenge ['skævəndʒ] v. 清除污物，打扫；（在废物中）寻觅

在一场船难中，唯一的幸存者随着潮水，漂流到了一座无人小岛上。他每天都发自肺腑地狂热祈祷，祈求上帝能够早日救他离开此处，让他回到家乡。他每天都注视着海上是否有可搭救他的人，但是除了汪洋一片，什么也没有。

后来，精疲力竭的他决定勉强建造一个简陋的小木屋，以便保护他在这险恶的环境中生存，并且帮他保存他所剩无几的东西。但是有一天，在他捕完食物、准备回小屋时，突然发现他的小屋竟然陷在熊熊烈火之中，大火引起的浓烟不断向天上窜去。

最糟糕的是：他剩下的所有东西，在这一瞬间通通化为乌有了。

对此他十分震惊。悲痛的他愤怒地对着上天呐喊道："神啊！你怎么可以能这样对我！"

然而，第二天一早，他被一艘正靠近小岛的船只的鸣笛声惊醒了。是的，有人来救他了。这个疲惫的人问那些救援人员："你们怎么知道我在这里？""因为我们看到了你的浓烟信号。"他们回答说。

they replied.

It is easy to get discouraged when things are going bad.

But we shouldn't lose heart, because God is at work in our lives, even in the midst of pain and suffering.

Remember, next time your little hut is burning to the ground it just may be a smoke signal that summons the grace of God.

For all the negative things we have to say to ourselves, God has a positive answer for it.

人在碰到困难时，很容易会泄气。

但是，无论遭受什么样的痛苦和折磨，都不要因此而失去信心，因为上帝一直在我们的生命中做着他的工作。

记住：下一次你的小木屋被夷为平地的时候，那可能只是烟雾信号呼求上帝恩典的时候。

对于所有我们认为负面的事情，我们都该告诉自己：上帝都是有正面答案的。

静谧动人的声音

The hardest arithmetic to master is that which enables us to count our blessings.

世界上最难的算术题就是如何清点我们的祝福。

A Child's Dream of a Star
一个孩子的星星梦

◎ Charles Dickens

There was once a child and he strolled about a good deal, and thought of a number of things. He had a sister, who was a child too, and his constant companion. These two used to wonder all day long. They wondered at the beauty of the flowers; they wondered at the height and blueness of the sky; they wondered at the depth of the bright water; they wondered at the goodness and the power of God who made the lovely world.

They used to say to one another, sometimes, supposing all the children upon earth were to die, would the flowers, and the water, and the sky be sorry? They believed they would be sorry. For, said they, the buds are the children of the flowers, and the little playful streams that gambol down the hill-sides are the children of the water; and the smallest bright specks playing at hide and seek in the sky all night, must surely be the children of the stars; and they would all be grieved to see their playmates, the children of men, no more.

There was one clear shining star that used to come out in the sky before the rest, near the church spire, above the graves. It was larger and more beautiful,

从前有个小男孩，四处漫步闲逛，脑子里想着各种各样的事情。他有个姐姐，也是个小孩子，是他最忠实的伙伴。他们常常终日遐想。他们惊叹花儿的美丽，惊叹天空的高远和蔚蓝，惊叹清澈河水的幽深，惊叹这个可爱世界的创造者——上帝——的仁慈和力量。

他们经常这样问彼此："假如世界上的小孩子都死了，花儿、河水和天空会感到难过吗？"他们坚信，它们会感到难过的。因为他们说过："花蕾是花的孩子；山谷里欢快的小溪是河水的孩子；整夜不睡觉在天上玩捉迷藏的小亮点，一定是星星的孩子；如果它们再也看不到自己的伙伴——人类的孩子，它们一定都会伤心难过。"

每天夜晚，在教堂的顶尖附近，在墓地的上空，总有一颗闪亮的星星先于其他星星出现在夜空中。在他们眼中，它比其他星星都更大更美。每天夜晚，他们都手拉着手站在窗前守候着它。无论谁先看到那颗星星，都会大声喊道："我看见星星啦！"但他们常常同时喊出这句话，因为他们太

they thought, than all the others, and every night they watched for it, standing hand in hand at a window. Whoever saw it first cried out, "I see the star!" And often they cried out both together, knowing so well when it would rise, and where. So they grew to be such friends with it, that, before lying down in their beds, they always looked out once again, to bid it good-night; and when they were turning round to sleep, they used to say, "God bless the star!"

But while she was still very young, oh very, very young, the sister drooped, and came to be so weak that she could no longer stand in the window at night; and then the child looked sadly out by himself, and when he saw the star, turned round and said to the patient pale face on the bed, "I see the star!" and then a smile would come upon the face, and a little weak voice used to say, "God bless my brother and the star!"

And so the time came all too soon! When the child looked out alone, and when there was no face on the bed; and when there was a little grave among the graves, not there before; and when the star made long rays down toward him, as he saw it through his tears.

Now, these rays were so bright, and they seemed to make such a shining way from earth to Heaven, that when the child went to his solitary bed, he dreamed about the star; and dreamed that, lying where he was, he saw a train of people taken up that sparkling road by angels. And the star, opening, showed him a great world of light, where many more such angels waited to receive them.

All these angels, who were waiting, turned their beaming eyes upon the people who were carried up into the star; and some came out from the long rows in which they stood, and fell upon the people's necks, and kissed them tenderly,

熟悉它升起的时间和地方了。于是，他们慢慢地成为了它的好朋友。每天临睡前，他们都要探出头再看它一眼，向它道声晚安；当他们转身准备入睡时，他们会念上一句："上帝保佑星星！"

可是他的姐姐，还很年轻的，非常年轻的姐姐枯萎憔悴了。她变得很虚弱，再也无法站在窗前看星星。于是，那个小男孩只好一个人伤心地望着窗外。每当他看到那颗星星时，他就会转身对着床上那张苍白的面孔说："我看见星星了！"接着，一丝微笑掠过她的脸，一个微弱的声音答道："愿上帝保佑我的弟弟和星星！"

不幸的时刻终于还是来了，一切都来得太过突然。从此小男孩独自一人望着窗外；从此床上不再有任何脸庞；从此墓地里又多了一座从前没有的小小坟墓。每当他满眼泪光地望着那颗星星时，星星的光芒就会洒在他的身上。

如今，这些光芒是那么的耀眼，仿佛铺开了一条通往天堂的星光大道。当小男孩独自一人睡在自己的床上时，他梦见了那颗星星，梦见自己躺在床上，看见一群人在天使的带领下走上那条星光大道。然后那颗星星打开了，一个光明的世界出现在他眼前，还有许多这样的天使正在恭候着他们。

这些恭候在此的天使们，用它们愉快的目光注视着这些被带到星星上的人们。有些天使从长长的队伍中飞出来，落在人们的脖子上，温柔地亲吻着，然后带领他们沿着星光大道离开了，他们在一起时很开心。躺在床上的小男孩高兴得哭了。

可还有一些天使没有和他们一起离开，其中有一张小男孩熟悉的脸庞。那张曾经躺在床上的苍白脸庞，现在已变得光彩照人。可他十分确定那就

and went away with them down avenues of light, and were so happy in their company, that lying in his bed he wept for joy.

But, there were many angels who did not go with them, and among them one he knew. The patient face that once had lain upon the bed was glorified and radiant, but his heart found out his sister among all the host.

His sister's angel lingered near the entrance of the star, and said to the leader among those who had brought the people thither:

"Is my brother come?"

And he said "No."

She was turning hopefully away, when the child stretched out his arms, and cried, "O, sister, I am here! Take me!" and then she turned her beaming eyes upon him, and it was night; and the star was shining into the room, making long rays down towards him as he saw it through his tears.

From that hour forth, the child looked out upon the star as on the home he was to go to, when his time should come; and he thought that he did not belong to the earth alone, but to the star too, because of his sister's angel gone before.

There was a baby born to be a brother to the child; and while he was so little that he never yet had spoken word he stretched his tiny form out on his bed, and died.

Again the child dreamed of the open star, and of the company of angels, and the train of people, and the rows of angels with their beaming eyes all turned upon those people's faces.

Said his sister's angel to the leader:

"Is my brother come?"

And he said "Not that one, but another."

As the child beheld his brother's angel in her arms, he cried, "O, sister, I am

是自己的姐姐。

他的天使姐姐在星星的入口处徘徊着不愿离去，问那位把人们带上星星的天使长：

“我的弟弟来了吗？”

天使长答道：“没有。”

她满怀希望地转身准备离开，这时小男孩伸出双臂喊道：“噢！姐姐，我在这儿呢！带我走吧！”她转过身，满脸笑容地看着他。然后，天黑了，星光在房间里闪耀。当他满眼泪光地望着那颗星星时，星星的光芒就会洒在他的身上。

从那以后，小男孩每次看到那颗星星，就仿佛看到了自己死后将要回的家。他觉得自己不但属于人间，也属于那颗星星，因为他的天使姐姐就在那儿。

不久，一个小婴儿诞生了，小男孩有了一个弟弟。可是，他太小了，还没说过一句话，只在床上伸伸手脚就夭折了。

小男孩再一次梦见那颗敞开的星星、成群的天使和人们。那些天使正满脸笑容地注视着人们的脸庞。

他的天使姐姐向天使长问道：

“我的弟弟来了吗？”

天使长答道：“来了，但不是那个弟弟，是另外一个。”

当小男孩看到弟弟投入天使姐姐的怀抱时，他大声叫道：“噢！姐姐，我在这儿呢！带我走吧！”于是，她转过身，满脸笑容地看着他，那颗星星在闪耀。

here! Take me!" And she turned and smiled upon him, and the star was shining.

He grew to be a young man, and was busy at his books when an old servant came to him and said:

"Thy mother is no more. I bring her blessing on her darling son!"

Again at night he saw the star, and all that former company. Said his sister's angel to the leader:

"Is my brother come?"

And he said, "Thy mother!"

A mighty cry of joy went forth through all the star, because the mother was reunited to her two children. And he stretched out his arms and cried, "O, mother, sister, and brother, I am here! Take me!" And they answered him, "Not yet," and the star was shining.

He grew to be a man, whose hair was turning gray, and he was sitting in his chair by the fireside, heavy with grief, and with his face bedewed with tears, when the star opened once again. Said his sister's angel to the leader "Is my brother come?"

And he said, "Nay, but his maiden daughter."

And the man who had been the child saw his daughter, newly lost to him, a celestial creature among those three, and he said, "My daughter's head is on my sister's bosom, and her arm is around my mother's neck, and at her feet there is the baby of old time, and I can bear the parting from her, God be praised!"

And the star was shining.

Thus the child came to be an old man, and his once smooth face was wrinkled, and his steps were slow and feeble, and his back was bent. And one

他渐渐长大了，成了一个年轻人。一天，他正在埋头苦读。这时，一位老仆人走近他，说道：

“您的母亲去世了，我带来了她对心爱儿子的真心祝福！”

那天夜里，他又梦见了那颗星星，还有从前梦里的那些天使和人们。他的天使姐姐向天使长问道：

“我的弟弟来了吗？”

天使长答道：“没有，你的妈妈来了。”

一声喜悦的惊呼响彻整个星星，因为妈妈再次和自己的两个孩子团聚了。小男孩伸出双臂喊道：“噢！妈妈，姐姐，弟弟，我在这儿呢！带我走吧！”只听见他们齐声答道：“现在还不行。”那颗星星依旧在闪耀。

渐渐地，他步入中年，头发也慢慢地发白了。一天，他心情沉重地坐在壁炉旁的安乐椅上，泪水打湿了脸庞。这时，星星的大门再一次打开了。他的天使姐姐向天使长问道：“我的弟弟来了吗？”

天使长答道：“没有，但是他尚未出嫁的女儿来了。”

这个曾经是小男孩的中年人看到了自己刚刚失去的女儿，一个天国里的新生灵，就在三位亲人的中间。他说道：“我女儿的头正倚在我姐姐的胸前，她的胳膊环绕在我母亲的脖子上，她的脚边是那位旧时的婴儿。感谢上帝！我可以忍受与她分离了。”

那颗星星依旧在闪耀。

就这样，小男孩变成了一位老人，曾经嫩滑的脸庞也爬满了皱纹，脚步也迟缓无力，背也驼了。一天晚上，他躺在自己的床上，子女围绕在他身旁。他大喊了一声，就像很久很久以前那样喊道：

night as he lay upon his bed, his children standing round, he cried, as he had cried so long ago:

"I see the star!"

They whispered one to another, "He is dying."

And he said, "I am. My age is falling from me like a garment, and I move towards the star as a child. And O, my Father, now I thank Thee that it has so often opened, to receive those dear ones who await me!"

And the star was shining, and it shines upon his grave.

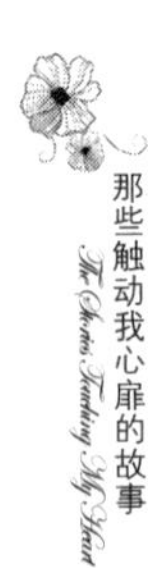

“我看见星星啦！”

他的子女在一旁低声说道：“他快要走了。”

他答道：“是的。我的大限将至，就像一件外套就快要从我身上滑落了。我就要作为一个小男孩走向那颗星星了。噢！主啊，我要感谢你，感谢那颗时常敞开的星星，收留等待我的亲人们！”

那颗星星在闪耀，一直闪耀在他的坟墓上方。

Dining with Mr. Yepp, a Smiling Face in the Cafeteria
餐厅的笑脸——让叶普先生伴你用餐

◎ Anonymous

I was a freshman in college when I met Mr. Yepp. He was friendly and smiled a lot. He was almost always standing by the cashier that checked us into the university cafeteria, and I would run into Mr. Yepp during three of my daily meals.

However, as the years past, I became annoyed by him. He would stand there and shake every person's hand that came through the cafeteria. This was a problem for me because I did not want to offend him by refusing his handshake; however, I did not want to shake hands with him before coming into the cafeteria to eat because he was shaking every single person's hand, and I had **sanitary**① concerns. When we had the **swine flu**② outbreak at the university, I started to avoid him by going through the back door.

I am out of college now, working full-time, and Mr. Yepp is still standing by the cashier doing the same thing that he has been doing for many years. A few weeks ago, I took some time to sit down and talk with him. It turns out he is not

① sanitary ['sænɪˌtɛri] a. 卫生的；清洁的

② swine flu [swaɪn flu] n. 猪流感

遇见叶普先生是在我大学一年级的时候。他时常面带友善的笑容，几乎总会站在门口和收银员一起迎接我们走进学校餐厅，因此，我一日三餐都会碰到叶普先生。

年复一年如此这般，我开始讨厌他了。他站在那里迎来送往，要和每一个从他身旁经过的人握手。出于卫生的考虑，我并不想在进餐厅用餐前握他的手，因为那双手和每个人都接触过，但如何拒绝又不冒犯他成了我的困扰。所以，当校园爆发猪流感时，我不得不绕走餐厅后门来躲避他。

如今，我已走出校门参加工作，而叶普先生还站在同样的位置做着这些年来重复在做的事。几个星期前，我有机会和他一起坐下来聊天，这时我才知道他在餐厅工作并没有薪水，可他却自愿为大家服务。我们总能看到他在学生离去后收拾餐桌的身影，有时还会站在门口顶替收银员的工作。

on the payroll, and he comes to the cafeteria of his own free will. Many times one may see him cleaning up after the students, and he sometimes even fills in for the cashier at the door, so I was surprised to learn that he is not a paid employee. When I asked him what motivated him to do what he does, he told me that he enjoys the stress-free environment. He is 79 years old but looks to be in his 50's. He retired many years ago and comes to the cafeteria to keep his mind and body active.

I noticed that he always takes a to-go plate before leaving the cafeteria. It turns out that he takes this plate home to his wife, who suffers from **dementia**[①]. I asked him about her, and he told me that he wakes up every morning at the same time, makes her breakfast, then leaves the house to give her space, which he says they both need, and he returns in the evening with dinner. He says that she took such great care of him when they were young and that he does the same for her now.

I asked Mr. Yepp, "Is a college campus really less stressful?" His answer was that he enjoys seeing and interacting with the young kids who have so much potential. After my talk with Mr. Yepp, I was embarrassed to have had the thoughts I had about his kindness. It never occurred to me that many times, he was probably the first smiling face that many students at the university saw in the morning, or that his speaking to everyone who walks into the cafeteria is a gesture that probably means a lot to many of the students, whose days he brightens. So now every time I run into Mr. Yepp, I make it a point to stop, give him a **high five**[②], and smile before moving on. Mr. Yepp spends an average of 8

① dementia [dɪ'mɛnʃə] n. 痴呆
② high five（运动员等相互间致意用的）举手击掌

知道他做这一切都是义务的时，我很吃惊。问他出于什么这样做，他告诉我，他喜欢这里轻松的氛围。他已经 79 岁高龄了，但看起来却还像 50 来岁的人。多年前他离休后就一直在餐厅帮忙，浑身上下都充满了活力。

我留意到，他从餐厅走时总会带上一个餐盒。原来，他是带给家中患有痴呆症的妻子的。聊到妻子，他告诉我说，每天早晨他都会准时起床，为她做好早饭后才出门。白天让她独处，也是给双方都留些彼此所需的空间。而到了晚上，他会带晚饭回家。他说，年轻时她给了他那么多的关爱，现在是他回报的时候了。

我问叶普先生："在大学校园里真的会感到放松吗？"他回答道，他愿意看着这些前景无限的年轻人，乐于跟他们交流。经过这番对话，我为自己曾经那样质疑他的善举而羞赧。我也第一次认识到，不知多少回，他都是学生们在清晨见到的第一张笑脸；他亲切地问候每一个走进餐厅的人，这举动或许正抚慰了那些心灵，照亮着他们的生活。如今，每当我碰到叶普先生，都会刻意停下脚步，举起手来跟他击掌致意，报以微笑才继续前

hours a day just to be a smiling face in the cafeteria. He can be seen going from table to table and speaking words of encouragement to many young men and women.

So today I name Mr. Yepp one of our many "Everyday Angels".

行。多年如一日，每天平均 8 小时，叶普先生化身为餐厅中的一张笑脸，他的身影穿梭于餐桌间，用勖勉的话语陪伴了许许多多的年轻人。

因此今天，我要将叶普先生命名为我们的一个“守护天使”。

The Gift of the Magi (Ⅰ)
麦琪的礼物（1）

◎ O. Henry

One dollar and eighty-seven cents. That was all. And sixty cents of it was in pennies. Pennies saved one and two at a time by bulldozing the grocer and the vegetable man and the butcher until one's cheeks burned with the silent imputation of parsimony that such close dealing implied. Three times Della counted it. One dollar and eighty-seven cents. And the next day would be Christmas.

There was clearly nothing to do but flop down on the shabby little couch and howl. So Della did it. Which instigates the moral reflection that life is made up of sobs, sniffles, and smiles, with sniffles predominating.

While the mistress of the home is gradually subsiding from the first stage to the second, take a look at the home. A furnished flat at $8 per week. It did not exactly beggar description, but it certainly had that word on the lookout for the mendicancy squad.

In the vestibule below was a letter-box into which no letter would go, and an

1 美元 87 美分。多一分钱都没有了。其中 60 美分还是一分分的零钱凑起来的。虽然深感在买卖时分毫必争实在丢人现眼，但这些零钱仍是她红着脸从杂货店老板、菜贩和屠夫那儿讨价还价，一分两分地攒下来的。德拉数了三遍。的确是 1 美元 87 美分。可明天就是圣诞节了。

除了扑倒在破旧的小沙发上大哭一场，显然再无别的应对之法。德拉的确就是这样。这就使一种精神上的思考就此而生——世俗生活是由哽咽、抽泣和微笑组成的，而抽泣总是处于支配地位。

这位主妇的心情逐渐平复了下来，让我们扫视一下她的家吧。一套每周 8 美元租金的公寓，自带家具。要说它是乞丐窝有点夸张，可从外观上看，其实也差不远。

楼下的过道里有个永远不会收到信的邮箱，还有一个永远也不会被按响的电铃。那儿还有一张名片，上面写着“詹姆斯 · 迪林厄姆 · 杨先生”。

“迪林厄姆”这个名号，是主人在每周 30 美元的辉煌日子时趁着兴子加上去的。如今，他的收入缩减到了 20 美元，他们也开始严肃地考虑，是

electric button from which no mortal finger could coax a ring. Also appertaining thereunto was a card bearing the name "Mr. James Dillingham Young".

The "Dillingham" had been flung to the breeze during a former period of prosperity when its possessor was being paid $30 per week. Now, when the income was shrunk to $20, though, they were thinking seriously of contracting to a modest and unassuming D. But whenever Mr. James Dillingham Young came home and reached his flat above he was called "Jim" and greatly hugged by Mrs. James Dillingham Young, already introduced to you as Della. Which is all very good.

Della finished her cry and attended to her cheeks with the powder rag. She stood by the window and looked out dully at a gray cat walking a gray fence in a gray backyard. Tomorrow would be Christmas Day, and she had only $1.87 with which to buy Jim a present. She had been saving every penny she could for months, with this result. Twenty dollars a week doesn't go far. Expenses had been greater than she had calculated. They always are. Only $1.87 to buy a present for Jim. Her Jim. Many a happy hour she had spent planning for something nice for him. Something fine and rare and sterling—something just a little bit near to being worthy of the honor of being owned by Jim.

There was a pier-glass between the windows of the room. Perhaps you have seen a pier-glass in an $8 flat. A very thin and very agile person may, by observing his reflection in a rapid sequence of longitudinal strips, obtain a fairly accurate conception of his looks. Della, being slender, had mastered the art.

Suddenly she whirled from the window and stood before the glass. Her eyes were shining brilliantly, but her face had lost its color within twenty seconds.

否应该把自己缩写成谦逊而务实的 D。但每当詹姆斯·迪林厄姆·杨先生回家走进楼上的房间时，詹姆斯·迪林厄姆·杨太太——就是刚刚为大家介绍的德拉——总会叫他一声“吉姆”，给他一个最热烈的拥抱。一切都非常完好。

德拉慢慢停止了哭泣，又往脸上抹了点粉。她站在窗前，两眼无神地看着一只爬行在昏暗后院里灰白篱笆上的灰白色的猫。明天就是圣诞了，而德拉能用来给吉姆买礼物的钱总共也只有 1 美元 87 美分。过去的几个月，她费尽心思用最大的努力一分分地攒积下来，却只有这点点钱。一周区区 20 美元的收入的确入不敷出，支出总是大于预算。因此，能给她心爱的吉姆买圣诞礼物的钱，也只有这 1 美元 87 美分。她无时无刻不在幸福地幻想着要送爱人一件称心的礼物，一件精致、稀有、贵重的礼物——至少是些配得上吉姆的东西才行。

房间的窗户与窗户之间有一面镜子。也许你可以想象到周租 8 美元公寓里的镜子。哪怕是一个非常瘦小的人，也得不断转动着观察从那狭长的镜子里投射出来的影像，才可能看得清自己的样貌。而苗条瘦弱的德拉也早已习惯这么做了。

突然，她从窗户边回过身来，立在了镜子跟前。她两眼目光闪烁，可不到二十秒，她的面色却失去了神色。她将头发迅速放下，让它们完全垂

Rapidly she pulled down her hair and let it fall to its full length.

Now, there were two possessions of the James Dillingham Youngs in which they both took a mighty pride. One was Jim's gold watch that had been his father's and his grandfather's. The other was Della's hair. Had the queen of Sheba lived in the flat across the airshaft, Della would have let her hair hang out the window some day to dry just to depreciate Her Majesty's jewels and gifts. Had King Solomon been the janitor, with all his treasures piled up in the basement, Jim would have pulled out his watch every time he passed, just to see him pluck at his beard from envy.

So now Della's beautiful hair fell about her rippling and shining like a cascade of brown waters. It reached below her knee and made itself almost a garment for her. And then she did it up again nervously and quickly. Once she faltered for a minute and stood still while a tear or two splashed on the worn red carpet.

On went her old brown jacket; on went her old brown hat. With a whirl of skirts and with the brilliant sparkle still in her eyes, she fluttered out the door and down the stairs to the street.

Where she stopped the sign read: "Mne. Sofronie. Hair Goods of All Kinds." One flight up Della ran, and collected herself, panting. Madame, large, too white, chilly, hardly looked the "Sofronie".

"Will you buy my hair?" asked Della.

"I buy hair," said Madame. "Take yer hat off and let's have a sight at the looks of it."

Down rippled the brown cascade.

落下来。

现在，让我们来看看詹姆斯·迪林厄姆·杨夫妇各自拥有的一件为之自豪的物品。吉姆有一块从祖父那儿传下来的金表；而德拉拥有的则是一头美丽无比的秀发。如果示巴女王住在风井对面的房间里，那德拉全然可以把洗完后的秀发抛出窗外晾晒，只为一比女王的金银珠宝；如果所罗门是这里的门房，那每当吉姆从他面前走过时定会从怀里摸出表来，让那把财富塞满地下室的所罗门王嫉妒得扯胡子。

此刻，德拉披散而下的秀发如同涟漪波浪，如棕色瀑布般倾泻而下。她的美发长及膝下，如一袭长袍加身。接着，她又紧张而迅速地把头发扎好。她有过那么一分钟的犹豫，当她呆站原地之时，几颗眼泪滴上了破旧的红毯。

她穿上她的棕色旧外套，戴上棕色旧帽子，眼里残留着晶莹的泪花，裙角一摆，便晃悠着出门、下楼、上街。

她在一块招牌前停了下来，上面写着："索夫罗尼夫人，各类发制品"。德拉箭步跑去，缓了缓气，定了定神。里面是一位肥胖的女士，肤色惨白冰冷，看上去简直不像"索夫罗尼"。

"您要买我的头发吗？"德拉询问道。

"我收购头发，"这位女士说，"把帽子摘掉，让我看看你的头发。"

棕色瀑布倾泻下来。

"20 美元。"这位夫人用一只老练的手掂了掂头发，说道。

"快把钱给我吧。"德拉说。

"Twenty dollars," said Madame, lifting the mass with a practised hand.

"Give it to me quick," said Della.

Oh, and the next two hours tripped by on rosy wings. Forget the hashed metaphor. She was ransacking the stores for Jim's present.

She found it at last. It surely had been made for Jim and no one else. There was no other like it in any of the stores, and she had turned all of them inside out. It was a platinum fob chain simple and chaste in design, properly proclaiming its value by substance alone and not by meretricious ornamentation—as all good things should do. It was even worthy of The Watch. As soon as she saw it she knew that it must be Jim's. It was like him. Quietness and value—the description applied to both. Twenty-one dollars they took from her for it, and she hurried home with the 87 cents. With that chain on his watch Jim might be properly anxious about the time in any company. Grand as the watch was, he sometimes looked at it on the sly on account of the old leather strap that he used in place of a chain.

When Della reached home her intoxication gave way a little to prudence and reason. She got out her curling irons and lighted the gas and went to work repairing the ravages made by generosity added to love. Which is always a tremendous task, dear friends—a mammoth task.

Within forty minutes her head was covered with tiny, close-lying curls that made her look wonderfully like a truant schoolboy. She looked at her reflection in the mirror long, carefully, and critically.

"If Jim doesn't kill me," she said to herself, "before he takes a second look at me, he'll say I look like a Coney Island chorus girl. But what could I do—oh!

噢，之后的两个小时长出了愉快的翅膀，轻快地掠过。忘了这随口的比喻吧。她正于各家店铺里寻觅着送给吉姆的礼物。

她终于找到了。它一定是为吉姆量身定制的。她把所有店铺都翻遍了，各个商店都没有这么一件东西。一根简朴的白金表带。上面镌刻着一些简单的花纹。和所有优质物品一样，这是一只低调而华丽的简单表链，和那只金表交相辉映。在第一眼看到它时，她就知道这东西一定要戴在吉姆的手上才能相配。它就像吉姆本人，虽然低调但却满腹才华——这一形容对两者都挺适用。她花了 21 美元将表链买下，然后身揣剩下的 87 美分急忙赶回了家。有了表链的金表，无论何时何地，吉姆都能骄傲地看时间了。尽管这是一块异常珍贵的表，但之前苦于过于破旧的皮革表链，弄得吉姆有时只敢偷偷地看上一眼。

德拉回到家，稍微平复了一下狂喜的情绪，变得理智平静了些。她翻出烫发钳，打燃煤气炉，试图弥补这为爱失去的发型。这可真是件麻烦事，亲爱的朋友们——一项浩大的工程啊。

不到四十分钟，她的头上就已烫出一圈圈小卷发，这让她看起来像一名逃课的小学生。她长久地盯着镜子里的自己，小心而又仔细。

“我这个样子，”德拉自言自语地说，“在吉姆看第二眼之前，就算不至于气到把我宰掉，也会嫌弃我像个在康尼岛上负责合唱的小姑娘吧。但是

What could I do with a dollar and eighty-seven cents?"

At 7 o'clock the coffee was made and the frying-pan was on the back of the stove hot and ready to cook the chops.

除此之外我能做什么呢——唉，1 美元 87 美分又有什么用呢？”

7 点的时候，她就把咖啡煮好了，煎锅也已经放在了热烫的炉火上，准备煎晚餐吃的肉排。

The Gift of the Magi (Ⅱ)
麦琪的礼物（2）

◎ O. Henry

Jim was never late. Della doubled the fob chain in her hand and sat on the corner of the table near the door that he always entered. Then she heard his step on the stair away down on the first flight, and she turned white for just a moment. She had a habit for saying little silent prayer about the simplest everyday things, and now she whispered: “Please God, make him think I am still pretty.”

The door opened and Jim stepped in and closed it. He looked thin and very serious. Poor fellow, he was only twenty-two—and to be burdened with a family! He needed a new overcoat and he was without gloves.

Jim stopped inside the door, as immovable as a setter at the scent of quail. His eyes were fixed upon Della, and there was an expression in them that she could not read, and it terrified her. It was not anger, nor surprise, nor disapproval, nor horror, nor any of the sentiments that she had been prepared for. He simply stared at her fixedly with that peculiar expression on his face.

Della wriggled off the table and went for him.

“Jim, darling,” she cried, “don't look at me that way. I had my hair cut off

1 吉姆从不晚归。德拉手里握着那根表链，静坐在紧靠他进门位置的桌子一角。然后，她听见他的脚步声从楼下渐渐传来，有一瞬间她的面色都发白了。德拉总是习惯祈祷一些最简单的日常琐事，此时，她在心里默默许愿："保佑我啊上帝，让吉姆觉得我依然美丽。"

门开了，吉姆走进来，又关上了门。他显得十分瘦削，面色严肃。可怜的人啊，他才 22 岁——就得肩负起整个家庭！他需要买件新大衣，他连手套都没有。

吉姆在门口停下了脚步，像猎狗闻到了鹌鹑气味似的一动也不动。他的双眼锁定在德拉身上，专注的神情让德拉难以捉摸，这让她不寒而栗。那种眼神不是愤怒，也不是讶异，又不是伤心，更不是厌恶，而是一种让她始料未及的神态。他就这么，以这种特别的神情一直凝视着德拉。

德拉从桌子上扭了下来，朝他走去。

"吉姆，亲爱的，"她喊道，"别这样盯着我。我把头发剪来卖了，因为

and sold because I couldn't have lived through Christmas without giving you a present. It'll grow out again—you won't mind, will you? I just had to do it. My hair grows awfully fast. Say 'Merry Christmas!' Jim, and let's be happy. You don't know what a nice—what a beautiful, nice gift I've got for you."

"You've cut off your hair?" asked Jim, laboriously, as if he had not arrived at that patent fact yet even after the hardest mental labor.

"Cut it off and sold it," said Della. "Don't you like me just as well, anyhow? I'm me without my hair, ain't I?"

Jim looked about the room curiously.

"You say your hair is gone?" he said, with an air almost of idiocy.

"You needn't look for it," said Della. "It's sold, I tell you—sold and gone, too. It's Christmas Eve, boy. Be good to me, for it went for you. Maybe the hairs of my head were numbered," she went on with sudden serious sweetness, "but nobody could ever count my love for you. Shall I put the chops on, Jim?"

Out of his trance Jim seemed quickly to wake. He enfolded his Della. For ten seconds let us regard with discreet scrutiny some inconsequential object in the other direction. Eight dollars a week or a million a year—what is the difference? A mathematician or a wit would give you the wrong answer. The magi brought valuable gifts, but that was not among them. This dark assertion will be illuminated later on.

Jim drew a package from his overcoat pocket and threw it upon the table.

"Don't make any mistake, Dell," he said, "about me. I don't think there's anything in the way of a haircut or a shave or a shampoo that could make me like my girl any less. But if you'll unwrap that package you may see why you had me

我无法安度一个不送你礼物的圣诞节。它会再长起来的——你不介意的，对吗？我真的不得不这么做。我的头发长得可快了。说‘圣诞快乐’吧！吉姆，让我们开心点儿。你不知道这是一件多么棒——多么美丽别致的礼物！”

“你把头发剪了？”吉姆问着，问得有些费力，似乎他的大脑在经历高速运转之后都无法接受这个板上钉钉的事实。

“剪来卖了，”德拉说，“无论怎样，你不还是一样爱我吗？少了头发，我还是我，不是吗？”

吉姆好奇地环视了一眼房间。

“你是说你的头发没了？”他白痴似地问了一句。

“你就别找了，”德拉说，“告诉你吧，已经卖了——卖了就没有了。孩子，这是圣诞前夜。对我好一些，因为这都是为了你呀。也许我的头发数得清，”她的语气突然变得异常温柔，“但谁也数不清我对你的爱。我可以把肉排放锅上了吗，吉姆？”

吉姆如梦初醒，一把抱住德拉。此刻，让我们花上十秒钟，从另一个角度，以一种细致入微的眼光去审视那些看似微不足道的细节吧。一周 8 美元和一年百万美元——有什么差别呢？数学大师或知识分子都只能给出错误的答案。麦琪带来了珍贵的礼物，但那却不在其中。这句生涩的断言将在后文有所阐释。

吉姆从大衣口袋里掏出一个袋子，然后把它扔在了桌子上。

going a while at first."

White fingers and nimble tore at the string and paper. And then an ecstatic scream of joy; and then, alas! A quick feminine change to hysterical tears and wails, necessitating the immediate employment of all the comforting powers of the lord of the flat.

For there lay The Combs—the set of combs, side and back, that Della had worshipped long in a Broadway window. Beautiful combs, pure tortoise shell, with jewelled rims—just the shade to wear in the beautiful vanished hair. They were expensive combs, she knew, and her heart had simply craved and yearned over them without the least hope of possession. And now, they were hers, but the tresses that should have adorned the coveted adornments were gone.

But she hugged them to her bosom, and at length she was able to look up with dim eyes and a smile and say: "My hair grows so fast, Jim!"

And then Della leaped up like a little singed cat and cried, "Oh, oh!"

Jim had not yet seen his beautiful present. She held it out to him eagerly upon her open palm. The dull precious metal seemed to flash with a reflection of her bright and ardent spirit.

"Isn't it a dandy, Jim? I hunted all over town to find it. You'll have to look at the time a hundred times a day now. Give me your watch. I want to see how it looks on it."

Instead of obeying, Jim tumbled down on the couch and put his hands under the back of his head and smiled.

"Dell," said he, "let's put our Christmas presents away and keep em a while. They're too nice to use just at present. I sold the watch to get the money to buy

“可别误会我了，德尔，”他说，“我不认为世间能有什么东西会让我对我女孩儿的爱意降低分毫，无论剪发还是修面还是洗头。只是，一旦打开这个袋子，你就能看见你之所以让我失态的原因了。”

白皙的手指在绳子上轻快地舞动，袋子随之打开。紧接而来的是喜悦的尖叫，但在一瞬之后，噢！却又突然变成了歇斯底里的眼泪和痛苦，这楚楚可怜的样儿急需公寓的一家之主倾尽所有前来安慰。

桌上摆放着一套梳子——一整套梳子，包括梳鬓角的，梳后脑的，一应俱全。这曾是很久以前，当德拉经过百老汇的一个橱窗时就一见钟情的物品。这精致的发梳，显而易见是用纯度最高的玳瑁打造的，梳沿上面镶嵌着宝石——色调与她已经卖掉的秀发相得益彰。她知道，这套梳子价格不菲，因此她仅仅只是渴求，从未想过拥有。而在此刻，这都是她的了，遗憾的是，那最能匹配这精致礼物的美丽秀发已经难觅芳踪。

她仍然把发梳搂在了胸口，过了好久才扬起沾满泪水的眼睛，微笑着说：“我的头发长得挺快的，吉姆！”

随后，德拉像一只被烫到的小猫那样一跃而起，叫道：“喔！喔！”

吉姆还没有看过他的美丽礼物呢。她摊开的手掌迫不及待地伸向他，那块贵金属似乎正闪现着她热忱的心情和快乐的神态。

“它超棒的对吗，吉姆？我寻遍全城才找到它。你现在必须每天看一百次时间。把表给我，我要看看它挂上去会是什么样子。”

相反，吉姆一头倒在了沙发，双手背在脑袋下面，露出微笑。

“德尔，”他说，“让我们把圣诞礼物先扔一边吧。对于目前的生活而言，

your combs. And now suppose you put the chops on."

The magi, as you know, were wise men—wonderfully wise men—who brought gifts to the Babe in the manger. They invented the art of giving Christmas presents. Being wise, their gifts were no doubt wise ones, possibly bearing the privilege of exchange in case of duplication. And here I have lamely related to you the uneventful chronicle of two foolish children in a flat who most unwisely sacrificed for each other the greatest treasures of their house. But in a last word to the wise of these days let it be said that of all who give gifts these two were the wisest. Everywhere they are wisest. They are the magi. .

它们太过精致。我用卖金表的钱为你买了发梳。此刻，我建议你可以下肉排了。”

你们知道，麦琪是智者——充满智慧的贤人——他们给生在马槽里的耶稣带来了礼物。他们创造了赠送圣诞礼物的艺术。毫无疑问，智者的礼物定是最合适的礼物，若是礼物重复，兴许还能享受交换的优待。我在这里蹩脚地讲述了一对住在公寓里的傻孩子的平淡故事，他们极不理智地为对方献祭了家里最珍贵的宝物。然而，容我对眼下的聪明人说最后一句话，在所有互赠礼物的人中，这俩人最为明智。他们无处不明智。他们就是麦琪。

The Perfect Dog"
完美的狗

◎ Jan Peck

During summer vacations, I would volunteer at the vet's, so I'd seen a lot of dogs. Minnie was by far the funniest-looking dog I'd ever seen. Thin curly hair barely covered her sausage-shaped body. Her bugged-out eyes always seemed surprised. And her tail looked like a rat's tail.

She was brought to the vet to be put to sleep because her owners didn't want her anymore. I thought Minnie had a sweet personality, though. "No one should judge her by her looks," I thought. So the vet spayed her and gave her the necessary shots. Finally, I advertised Minnie in the local paper: "Funny-looking dog, well behaved, needs loving family."

When a young man called, I warned him that Minnie was strange looking. The boy on the phone told me that his grandfather's sixteen-year-old dog had just died. They wanted Minnie no matter what. I gave Minnie a good bath and fluffed up what was left of her scraggly hair. Then we waited for them to arrive.

At last, an old car drove up in front of the vet's. Two kids raced to the door. They scooped Minnie into their arms and rushed her out to their grandfather, who

暑假期间，我在宠物诊所当志愿者，所以平时可以看到很多小狗。米妮是我目前为止看到过长得最滑稽的狗。又细又卷的毛发勉强盖住她那腊肠般的身体。最近她凸出的眼睛常常看起来处于惊恐状，尾巴则像一条老鼠的尾巴。

由于主人的遗弃，她到兽医院来是准备被执行安乐死的。但我觉得，米妮的性格既活泼又可爱。我想："可不能只看她的外表。"接下来，兽医给她做了绝育手术，然后做了些必要的身体检查。最后，我在当地一家报社为米妮登了一份广告："滑稽可爱的小狗，性格温顺，寻一户充满爱的家庭。"

一个年轻男孩打来了认领电话，我提醒他说其实米妮的外型并不好看。男孩却在电话里告诉我，他的祖父有一条 16 岁高龄的狗狗，但不幸刚去世了。他们想要米妮，并不计较什么外表。于是我把米妮洗得干干净净，把她蓬乱的毛发理得顺滑整齐，然后等着男孩他们的到来。

之后，一辆老式轿车停在了宠物诊所的门前。两个孩子迫不及待地朝大门跑来。他们抓起米妮抱在怀里，朝着等在轿车里的祖父跑去。我赶紧

was waiting in the car. I hurried behind them to see his reaction to Minnie.

Inside the car, the grandfather cradled Minnie in his arms and stroked her soft hair. She licked his face. Her rattail wagged around so quickly that it looked like it might fly off her body. It was love at first lick.

"She's perfect!" the old man exclaimed.

I was thankful that Minnie had found the good home that she deserved. That's when I saw that the grandfather's eyes were a milky white color—he was blind.

跟在后面，想看看老人对米妮的反应。

车里，这位祖父环抱着米妮，轻抚着她柔软的毛发。米妮轻轻舔着老人的脸。她的“鼠尾巴”摇得飞快，看起来像快要从身体上飞出去一样。就这么一舔，爱已弥漫。

“她真完美！”老人赞叹着。

我发现这位祖父的眼球是乳白色的——他看不见。就在这一刻，我很感激，米妮终于找到了一个渴望已久的好归宿。

Chapter 3

震撼非凡的身影

I don't measure a man's success by how high he climbs but how high he bounces when he hits bottom.

一个人的成功不是看他爬得有多高，而是看他跌到谷底之后能反弹多高。

The Daffodil Principle
水仙花的启示

© Jaroldeen Asplundh Edwards

Several times my daughter had telephoned to say, "Mother, you must come see the daffodils before they are over." I wanted to go, but it was a two-hour drive from Laguna to Lake Arrowhead. "I will come next Tuesday," I promised, a little reluctantly, on her third call.

Next Tuesday dawned cold and rainy. Still, I had promised, and so I drove there. When I finally walked into Carolyn's house and hugged and greeted my grandchildren, I said, "Forget the daffodils, Carolyn! The road is invisible in the clouds and fog, and there is nothing in the world except you and these children that I want to see bad enough to drive another inch!"

My daughter smiled calmly and said, "We drive in this all the time, Mother."

"Well, you won't get me back on the road until it clears, and then I'm heading for home!" I assured her.

"I was hoping you'd take me over to the garage to pick up my car."

"How far will we have to drive?"

女儿几次打电话跟我说："妈妈，水仙花谢之前，您一定要记得来看看它们哦。"我倒是想去，但从拉古娜到箭头湖有两个半小时的车程。"我下周二会去。"虽然有点不情愿，但在女儿打来三次电话后，我还是向女儿这样承诺了。

到了周二，却是阴冷多雨的天气。然而，既然已经答应女儿，我还是驱车前往了。终于到达了卡洛琳的家，我和我的外孙们纷纷拥抱、彼此问候，我说："别想水仙花啦，卡洛琳！云雾遮住了道路，要不是为了见你和我的外孙们，我都撑不到这里。"

女儿淡淡地笑着说："妈妈，我们经常在这样的天气里开车呢。"

"除非雾散了我才去，而且之后我就要立刻开车回家！"我坚定地说。

"我希望您能载我到修车厂取车。"

"有多远？"

"就几条街而已。"卡洛琳回答。"我来开吧，我已经习惯这种天气了。"

"Just a few blocks," Carolyn said. "I'll drive. I'm used to this."

After several minutes, I had to ask, "Where are we going? This isn't the way to the garage!"

"We're going to my garage the long way," Carolyn smiled, "by way of the daffodils."

"Carolyn," I said sternly, "please turn around."

"It's all right, Mother, I promise. You will never forgive yourself if you miss this experience."

After about twenty minutes, we turned onto a small gravel road and I saw a small church. On the far side of the church, I saw a hand-lettered sign that said, "Daffodil Garden".

We got out of the car and each took a child's hand, and I followed Carolyn down the path. Then, we turned a corner of the path, and I looked up and gasped. Before me lay the most glorious sight. It looked as though someone had taken a great vat of gold and poured it down over the mountain peak and slopes. The flowers were planted in majestic, swirling patterns—great ribbons and swaths of deep orange, white, lemon yellow, salmon pink, saffron, and butter yellow. Each different-colored variety was planted as a group so that it swirled and flowed like its own river with its own unique hue. There were five acres of flowers.

"But who has done this?" I asked Carolyn.

"It's just one woman," Carolyn answered. "She lives on the property. That's her home." Carolyn pointed to a well kept A-frame house that looked small and modest in the midst of all that glory. We walked up to the house. On the patio, we saw a poster. "Answers to the Questions I Know You Are Asking" was the

几分钟后，我忍不住问她："我们要去哪儿？这不是去修理厂的路啊！"

女儿笑着回答："我们就是去修车厂的路啊，刚好会路过水仙花开的地方。"

"卡洛琳，"我很坚决地说道，"请你马上掉头！"

"没关系的，妈妈，我保证您不虚此行，如果错过这次赏花机会，您会终生遗憾的。"

20分钟后，我们转到了一条小石子路上，我看到了一座小教堂。绕到教堂的另一边，一块手写的牌子上写着"水仙公园"。

我们一手牵着一个孩子下了车，我一路上都紧跟着卡洛琳。接着，我们到达了小径的一角。我抬头一看，不禁倒吸一口冷气，这是多么辉煌的景象啊。就像是有人将一缸黄金倾倒在漫山遍野上。花朵灿烂盛开，花纹呈螺旋状——有像巨幅彩带的，深橘色，白色，柠檬黄，鲑鱼粉，藏红色，奶油黄……差不多5亩花田，每个不同颜色的品种作为一个群体来种植，看上去就像一条极具特色的河流，按自己的方式盘旋着，流动着。

"这些是谁的杰作？"我问卡洛琳。

"是一位女士，"卡洛琳回答，然后指着繁花簇锦深处，那儿隐藏着一栋虽然很小、却被保存得很好的A字型屋子，"这里都是她的地方。那儿就是她的家。"于是，我们朝着屋子走去。走到露台前，我们看到 张海

headline.

The first answer was a simple one. "50,000 bulbs," it read. The second answer was, "One at a time, by one woman. Two hands, two feet, and very little brain." The third answer was, "Began in 1958."

There it was, The Daffodil Principle. For me, that moment was a life-changing experience.

I thought of this woman whom I had never met, who, more than forty years before, had begun—one bulb at a time—to bring her vision of beauty and joy to an obscure mountain top. Still, just planting one bulb at a time, year after year, had changed the world. This unknown woman had forever changed the world in which she lived. She had created something of ineffable (indescribable) magnificence, beauty, and inspiration.

The principle her daffodil garden taught is one of the greatest principles of celebration. That is, learning to move toward our goals and desires one step at a time—often just one baby-step at a time—and learning to love the doing, learning to use the accumulation of time. When we multiply tiny pieces of time with small increments of daily effort, we too will find we can accomplish magnificent things. We can change the world.

"It makes me sad in a way," I admitted to Carolyn. "What might I have accomplished if I had thought of a wonderful goal thirty-five or forty years ago and had worked away at it 'one bulb at a time' through all those years. Just think what I might have been able to achieve!"

My daughter summed up the message of the day in her usual direct way. "Start tomorrow," she said.

报，标题为："答案——给那些我知道你想问的问题"。

第一个答案很简单："50,000 朵。"上面写着。第二个答案是："一位妇女，一次一颗，两只手，两只脚，带着最单纯的头脑。"第三个答案是："始于 1958 年。"

此刻，对于我来说，这些水仙花给了我足以改变人生观的启发。

我在头脑中描绘起这个素未谋面的妇女来，是她，在 40 年前就开始，一次一颗种子，把她对美丽和幸福的见解，播种在这片不起眼的高山之巅。就这样，一次一颗，年复一年，直至改变了整个世界。这位不知名的妇女竟然就这样把她居住的地方永久地改变了。她就这样创造了非凡的壮丽，又兼具了美感和灵感。

这片黄水仙给人最大的启发就是，学会一步一个脚印地朝目标和梦想进发——哪怕是婴儿般的一次一小步——我们还要学会热爱我们所坚持的，学习把握好时间，循序渐进。当这些一天一点的努力日积月累，我们也会发现，创造辉煌并非难事。谁都可以改变世界。

"这趟旅途让我有点怅然若失，"我向卡洛琳承认道。"如果我在 35 年或 40 年前，为一个美好的愿望，一天一点地付出并持之以恒，真是难以想象我现在已经有多么大的成就了！"

女儿用一贯直接的方式总结了今天的收获。她说："妈妈，那就从明天开始吧！"

Three Peach Stones
三棵核桃

◎ R. Duncan

Observe a child; any one will do. You will see that not a day passes in which he does not find something or other to make him happy, though he may be in tears the next moment. Then look at a man; any one of us will do. You will notice that weeks and months can pass in which day is greeted with nothing more than resignation, and endure with every polite indifference. Indeed, most men are as miserable as sinners though they are too bored to sin-perhaps their sin is their indifference. But it is true that they so seldom smile that when they do we do not recognize their face, so distorted is it from the fixed mask we take for granted. And even then a man can not smile like a child, for a child smiles with his eyes, whereas a man smiles with his lips alone. It is not a smile; but a grin; something to do with humor, but little to do with happiness. And then, as anyone can see, there is a point (but who can define that point?) when a man becomes an old man, and then he will smile again.

It would seem that happiness is something to do with simplicity, and that it is the ability to **extract**[①] pleasure form the simplest things—such as a peach stone

① extract [ɪk'strækt] v. 提取；取出

观察一个孩子，任何一个都行。你会发现，他们总会在一天中找到乐子，虽然下一秒可能就会哭哭啼啼。再看看一个成年人，我们当中的任何一个都行。你会注意到，人们月复一月、周复一周地生活在忍气吞声和冷冰冰的礼貌中。大多数人事实上就如罪人那样恐怖，尽管他们也厌弃犯罪——也许他们的罪恶就是他们的冷漠。他们不苟言笑，就算难得一笑，我们也分辨不出来；久而久之，我们就把这些脸当成了一张张僵硬的面具。成年人甚至不会像孩童那样笑；因为孩童的笑是用眼睛，而成年人的笑只会动动嘴唇。这不是笑，而是呲牙咧嘴；这可能很搞笑，但与快乐无关。还有，众说周知，当成年人步入老年之后，他又会笑了（其原因还无人知晓）。

幸福来源于简单，是一种从最简单的事物——比如说一枚核桃中汲取快乐的能力。

很显然，幸福与成功无关。亨利·斯图亚特爵士是一位杰出的成功人士。20 年前，他从伦敦来到我们的村庄，买了几间村舍，然后把它们合并

for instance.

It is obvious that it is nothing to do with success. For Sir Henry Stewart was certainly successful. It is twenty years ago since he came down to our village from London, and bought a couple of old cottages, which he had knocked into one. He used his house as weekend refuge. He was a barrister. And the village followed his brilliant career with something almost amounting to paternal pride.

I remember some ten years ago when he was made a King's Counsel, Amos and I, seeing him get off the London train, went to congratulate him. We grinned with pleasure; he merely looked as miserable as though he'd received a **penal sentence**[①]. It was the same when he was knighted; he never smiled a bit, he didn't even bother to celebrate with a round of drinks at the "Blue Fox". He took his success as a child does his medicine. And not one of his achievements brought even a ghost of a smile to his tired eyes.

I asked him one day, soon after he'd retired to potter about his garden, what it was like to achieve all one's ambitions. He looked down at his roses and went on watering them. Then he said, "The only value in achieving one's ambition is that you then realize that they are not worth achieving." Quickly he moved the conversation on to a more practical level, and within a moment we were back to a safe discussion on the weather. That was two years ago.

I recall this incident, for yesterday, I was passing his house, and had **drawn up**[②] my cart just outside his garden wall. I had pulled in from the road for no other reason than to let a bus pass me. As I set there filling my pipe, I suddenly

---

① penal sentence 刑事判决

② draw up 使（车、马等）停住；（车、马等）停下来

在一起。他把这里作为他周末的休养之处。他是一位讼务律师。看着他辉煌的成就，村里人怀着一种几近父辈的骄傲。

我记得约摸 10 年前，亨利成为了国王的法律顾问。我和阿莫斯去火车站送他，向他表示我们的祝贺。我们都开心地笑了，但他却一脸痛苦的样子，好像是被判了刑。他受封为爵士时也是这个样子。他从不开怀大笑，也不愿在“蓝狐”酒家喝酒庆祝。他获取成功就像是小孩吞了药一样。在他的成就之中，没有一个能让他疲惫的双眼增添一丝淡淡的笑意。

一天，他在他的花园里散步，我问他，达成自己的目标后是什么感觉。他没有理睬我，低头浇他的玫瑰。过了一会儿，他说，“实现自己抱负的唯一价值就是让你意识到它们根本不值得你去追求。”当他还要深入下去时，为了避免尴尬，我们还是转到了较为温和的话题上——天气。这番对话发生在两年前。

昨天，我路过亨利的宅子，把马车停在他的花园外。这时，我想起了那件事。我之所以把马车从大路边停到花园边，就是为了要给一辆公交车让路。在我往烟斗里添加烟草时，我突然听到了一阵笑声从围墙里面传出

heard a shout of sheer joy come from the other side of the wall.

I peered over. There stood Sir Henry doing nothing less than a tribal war dance of sheer unashamed ecstasy. Even when he observed my bewildered face staring over the wall he did not seem put out or **embarrassed**[①], but shouted for me to climb over.

"Come and see, Jan. Look! I have done it at last! I have done it at last!"

There he was, holding a small box of earth in his had. I observed three tiny shoots out of it.

"And there were only three!" he said, his eyes laughing to heaven.

"Three what?" I asked.

"Peach stones," he replied. "I've always wanted to make peach stones grow, even since I was a child, when I used to take them home after a party, or as a man after a banquet. And I used to plant them, and then forgot where I planted them. But now at last I have done it, and, what's more, I had only three stones, and there you are, one, two, three shoots," he counted.

And Sir Henry ran off, calling for his wife to come and see his achievement—his achievement of simplicity.

① embarrass [ɪm'bærəs] v. 使局促不安；使困窘

来。

我向围墙里张望，看到亨利手舞足蹈，一副欣喜若狂的样子。即使在他看到我困惑不解的样子时，他也没有停止跳舞，或是感到窘迫，还呼喊着让我爬围墙过来。

“简，来看看，我终于做成了，我终于做成了！”

我看到他手里握着一小盒泥土，里面有三棵幼嫩的小苗。

“这有三个呢！”他笑盈盈地说。

我问道：“三个什么？”

“三个核桃，”他补充道，“我一直想要种三棵核桃树。我小时候经常在聚会后把核桃种子带回家，成年了，就在宴会后这么做。我经常把它们种下去，之后就忘了种的地方。但现在终于成功了，你看，我有三棵核桃。”他认真地数着，“一个，两个，三个。”

亨利说完后就走开了，叫他的妻子也来看看他的成就——他从简单之处所获取的成功。

Dreams Do Come True

美梦终会成真

◎ Anonymous

As a child, my parents, by their example, **instilled**① in me a love for reading. I dreamed of being a writer but the pursuit of dreams was never discussed or encouraged––leaving me to write in secret in my room.

Life progressed, however, and an interest in interior design surfaced in my teens. However, at my parents' insistence, I enrolled in **secretarial**② school and worked in that area contentedly, for twenty years.

Married with two children at thirty-eight, I grew restless. I was unhappy with my job and felt exhausted at the end of the day. I wanted to do something creative with my life. "Life begins at forty" became my **mantra**③.

A growing addiction to decorating shows on television reawakened my teenage interest. As I devoured every word and every scene, I vowed that I would let nothing deter me from becoming an interior designer.

With my fortieth birthday ten months away, I signed up for a two-year interior-decorating course. I crammed two years of work into nine months

① instill [in'stil] v. 逐渐灌输；滴注

② secretarial [.sekrə'tɛriəl] a. 秘书的

③ mantra ['mʌntrə] n. 颂歌，咒语

小时候，我的父母，以他们自己为榜样，有意识地培养我对阅读的热爱。我梦想成为一名作家，但对这一梦想的追求，我从未与人讨论过，也从未受过他人的鼓励——我总是把自己关在房间里秘密地写作。

生活在不断地继续着。在十几岁的青少年时期，我忽然对室内设计产生了浓厚的兴趣。然而，在我父母的坚持下，我进入了秘书学校，并在这个领域心满意足地工作了 20 年。

婚后育有两个孩子、已经 38 岁的我开始变得焦躁不安。我不满意自己的工作，在一天结束的时候，时常感觉很疲惫。我想在生活中做些创造性的事情。于是，“生命始于四十”成了我的口头禅。

对电视装饰节目的日益沉迷唤醒了我十几岁时的兴趣。当我细细品味节目中的每一句话和每一个场景时，我发誓：我不允许任何东西阻碍我成为一名室内设计师。

离我 40 岁生日还有 10 个月时，我报名参加了一个为期两年的室内装

to ensure that I received my diploma for my fortieth birthday. I met my self-imposed deadline with twelve days to spare and I was ecstatic.

The next step was to get some hands-on experience at a design firm. A visit to a newly opened interiors showroom ushered me into a dream job that opened more opportunities for me than I could have ever imagined. I donned the hat of a decorating consultant at the showroom and I was on my way to creating the career I envisioned.

Opportunity knocked at my door in 1997. I peeked and saw the possibility of writing a decorating column for a woman's magazine. The editor liked the idea and the monthly column debuted in February 1998.

Writing did not only open doors for decorating projects, it also provided me with the opportunity to teach interior decorating classes. A three-year teaching experience added a new dimension to my career while the confidence and reputation I gained were invaluable.

In the midst of the enjoying my new career and the diversity of experiences, I realized that I was involved in doing something I dreamed of as a child. I was writing. To master the finer skills, I signed up for a freelance writing course. Encouraging feedback from tutors gave me the confidence to submit my work for publication on the internet.

An online newsletter published the story of my mission to redefine myself and pursue my dream. The response from readers was unexpected and overwhelming. From around the world, people emailed to say that they identified with my experience. Some even asked for advice. They inspired me to write self-care articles and motivational pieces, especially for women. Soon, this hobby had

饰课程。我把两年的课程挤压在 9 个月里完成，以保证在我 40 岁生日那天能获得文凭。离我自己设定的最后期限还有 12 天时，我圆满完成了任务。在那个时刻，我欣喜若狂。

下一个步骤，就是去设计公司工作以获得一些实践经验。我拜访了一间新开张的内饰陈列室，这次经历不仅带给我一份梦寐以求的工作，而且也为我开启了远远超出想象的更多机会。我在展厅戴上装饰顾问的帽子，感觉自己正在通往设想中的职业生涯的路上。

1997 年，我的机会终于来了。我稍微留意了一番，发现了为女性杂志编写装饰专栏的可能。编辑喜欢这个主意，并在 1998 年 2 月首次推出每月一期的装饰专栏。

专栏写作不仅为装饰项目开放了大门，也让我有机会从事室内装饰类的教学工作。为期三年的教学经验为我的事业添加了一个新的维度，我从中获得的信心和荣誉更是无比珍贵。

正当我享受崭新的事业和丰富多彩的经历时，我意识到我在做的事情实际上就是我小时候的梦想。我正在从事写作。为了掌握更好的写作技能，我报名参加了一个自由写作课程。导师鼓励性的反馈给了我信心，于是我将自己的作品发表在互联网上。

一家在线通讯发表了我重新定义自己、追求梦想的故事。读者的反应出人意料，反响巨大。来自世界各地的人们发电子邮件给我，告诉我说他们认同我的经历。一些人甚至要求我为他们提供建议。他们也激发了我去写作有关自爱励志的文章，尤其是针对女性。很快，这个爱好变成了一种

developed into a passion that consumed me—and my writing.

Nevertheless, working a fulltime job and struggling to write at night while fighting sleep and fatigue did not **whittle**[1] away at my determination to be a fulltime freelance writer. I hung on because I had another dream—to retire at fifty, even though my fifty-first birthday was staring me in the face.

Prompted by my husband and grown, working children, I handed in my resignation on the 8th of August 2006. The next day, knowing that I will have the time to do the kind of research and writing I enjoy, I sent my writing resume and copies of my published clips to the three local newspapers in my country. I contacted every editor I had worked with before to let them know that I would be available for assignments.

One week before I left, the oldest and largest newspaper in my country commissioned me to write a weekly motivational/inspirational column for their Sunday pullout magazine for women. On the 30th August 2006, eighteen days before I turned fifty-one, I left my office for the last time.

I now write two regular columns while researching and writing feature articles on a variety of other topics, mostly for publication in online magazines. Three books are works in progress and my website is under construction.

My family tells me that I look younger and seem more energetic. I am living my childhood dream, doing what I love. I am a fulltime freelance writer with yet another dream—to be a motivational speaker.

On my journey, I have learned that it is never too late to pursue, and live your dream.

---

① whittle ['witl] v. 削（木头）；削减

激情，萦绕着我和我的写作。

然而，拥有一份全职工作的同时，努力在夜间写作、对抗睡意和疲倦，这并没有削弱我成为一个全职自由撰稿人的决心。我能坚持下去，因为我有另一个梦想——在 50 岁时退休，尽管我的 51 岁生日已近在眼前。

由于我的丈夫以及已经长大并工作了的孩子们不停地怂恿，2006 年 8 月 8 日，我提交了我的辞呈。因为我知道辞职后将会有充足的时间从事我喜欢的研究和写作，第二天，我就把我写作的简历、发表的文章复印件寄给了三份当地报纸。我联系了每一个之前共事过的编辑，告知他们我可以接受他们的约稿。

在我离职的前一周，国内历史最悠久、规模最大的报纸委托我为他们周日附送的女性杂志撰写每周励志专栏。2006 年 8 月 30 日，我终于告别了我的办公室，并且不再回来。那一天，离我的 51 岁生日只有 18 天了。

我现在在两个常规专栏发表文章，同时研究和写作其他各种主题的专题文章，主要发表在网络杂志上。三本书的写作正在进展中，我的网站也正在建设中。

我的家人告诉我，我看起来似乎更年轻、更有活力了。我实现了我童年的梦想，做了我喜欢的事情：我是一名全职自由撰稿人，我还梦想成为一名励志演说家。

从我的生活轨迹中，我已经学会了一条真理：追求并实现你的梦想，永远都不会太迟。

Overcoming Adversity: Find What You Love
扭转逆境：找到你的至爱

◎ Steve Jobs

I am honored to be with you today at your commencement from one of the finest universities in the world. I never graduated from college. Truth be told, this is the closest I've ever gotten to a college graduation. Today I want to tell you three stories from my life. That's it. No big deal. Just three stories.

The first story is about connecting the dots. I dropped out of Reed College after the first 6 months. So why did I drop out? It started before I was born. My biological mother was a young, unwed college graduate student, and she decided to put me up for adoption. She felt very strongly that I should be adopted by college graduates. My biological mother later found out that my mother had never graduated from college and that my father had never graduated from high school. She refused to sign the final adoption papers. She only relented a few months later when my parents promised that I would someday go to college.

And 17 years later I did go to college. But I naively chose a college that was almost as expensive as Stanford, and all of my working-class parents' savings were being spent on my college tuition. After six months, I couldn't see the value

今天，能与你们一起参加毕业典礼，我深感荣幸。你们即将从世界上最顶尖的大学毕业。而我从未大学毕业。说实话，今天算是我最接近大学毕业的时刻。我想要跟你们分享我生活中的三个故事。仅此而已。没什么大不了的东西，只是三个故事而已。

第一个故事是关于连接人生的节点。我在里德大学仅上了六个月使退学了。我为什么要退学呢？这得从我出生之前开始说起。我的生母是一名年轻未婚的在校研究生，她决定将我送给别人收养，并强烈坚持我应该被大学毕业生收养。我的生母后来发现，我的养母大学没有毕业，我的养父连高中都没有毕业。她就拒绝签这个收养合同。几个月后，我的养父母同意将来一定会送我上大学，她的态度才缓和下来。

17 年后，我的确上大学了。但是我很无知地选了一所学费几乎跟斯坦福一样贵的大学。我那工薪阶层的养父母把所有的积蓄都花在了我的学费上。六个月后，我看不到其中的价值所在。我不知道我想过什么样的生

in it. I had no idea what I wanted to do with my life...and here I was spending all of the money my parents had saved their entire life. So I decided to drop out and trust that it would all work out OK. It was pretty scary at the time, but looking back it was one of the best decisions I ever made. The minute I dropped out I could stop taking the required classes that didn't interest me, and begin dropping in on the ones that looked interesting.

Reed College at that time offered perhaps the best **calligraphy**[①] instruction in the country. Throughout the campus every poster, every label on every drawer, was beautifully hand calligraphed. Because I had dropped out and didn't have to take the normal classes, I decided to take a calligraphy class to learn how to do this. I learned about serif and san serif typefaces, about varying the amount of space between different letter combinations, about what makes great typography great.

None of this had even a hope of any practical application in my life. But ten years later, when we were designing the first Macintosh computer, it all came back to me. And we designed it all into the Mac. It was the first computer with beautiful typography. If I had never dropped in on that single course in college, the Mac would have never had multiple typefaces or proportionally spaced fonts.

My second story is about love and loss. I was lucky—I found what I loved to do early in life. Woz and I started Apple in my parents' garage when I was 20. We worked hard, and in 10 years Apple had grown from just the two of us in a garage into a $2 billion company with over 4,000 employees. We had just released our finest creation—the Macintosh—a year earlier, and I had just turned

① calligraphy [kə'ligrəfi] n. 书法

活……而这时，我就要花光父母的终生积蓄。所以我决定退学，并且相信未来一切都会好的。那时我感到非常害怕，但是现在回想起来，这是我做出的最正确的决定之一。从退学那一刻起，我可以跳过不感兴趣的必修课，而开始旁听一些看上去有意思的课。

里德学院在那时提供的也许是全美最好的美术字课程。学院里面的每张海报、每个抽屉的标签上全都是漂亮的手写美术字。因为我已经退学，不用再去上那些常规的课程，于是我选择了一个书法班，想学学怎么写美术字。我学到了衬线字体和无衬线字体，也学到了不同字母组合之间的间距变化，以及如何做出漂亮的版式。

似乎我一辈子也不太可能实际应用这些知识。但 10 年之后，当我们在设计第一台苹果电脑时，这一切都重新出现在我脑海里。我们将其全都设计进了苹果电脑，第一台有漂亮字体的电脑。如果我没有旁听那样一门课里，苹果电脑可能就不会有多重字体，也不会有等比例间距字体。

我的第二个故事是关于爱和失去。我很幸运——我在人生早期就发现自己喜欢做什么。20 岁的时候，我和沃兹在我父母的车库里开创了苹果公司。我们努力工作，10 年之后，苹果已经从只有我们两人的车库里发展成了一个 20 亿美元的公司，员工人数超过 4,000 人。我们推出了我们最好的创造——苹果电脑——而就在一年前，我刚过而立之年。然后我被炒鱿鱼

30. And then I got fired. How can you get fired from a company you started?

I really didn't know what to do for a few months. I was a very public failure, and I even thought about running away from the valley. But something slowly began to dawn on me—I still loved what I did. I had been rejected, but I was still in love. And so I decided to start over. I didn't see it then, but it turned out that getting fired from Apple was the best thing that could have ever happened to me. The heaviness of being successful was replaced by the lightness of being a beginner again, less sure about everything. It freed me to enter one of the most creative periods of my life.

During the next five years, I started a company named NeXT, another company named Pixar, and fell in love with an amazing woman who would become my wife. Pixar went on to create the worlds first computer animated feature film, Toy Story, and is now the most successful animation studio in the world. In a remarkable turn of events, Apple bought NeXT, I retuned to Apple, and the technology we developed at NeXT is at the heart of Apple's current **renaissance**[①]. And Laurene and I have a wonderful family together.

I'm pretty sure none of this would have happened if I hadn't been fired from Apple. It was awful tasting medicine, but I guess the patient needed it. Sometimes life hits you in the head with a brick. Don't lose faith. I'm convinced that the only thing that kept me going was that I loved what I did. You've got to find what you love. And that is as true for your work as it is for your lovers.

My third story is about death. When I was 17, I read a quote that went something like: "If you live each day as if it was your last, someday you'll most

① renaissance [rə'neisəns] n. 文艺复兴；再生

了。你怎么可能被你自己创立的公司炒了鱿鱼呢?

接下去的几个月里，我真的不知道该做什么。我成了人人皆知的失败者，甚至一度想逃离硅谷。但事情渐渐明朗起来——我还是喜欢我做过的事情。虽然我被驱逐了，但是我仍然钟爱它。于是，我决定从头再来。后来的事实证明，从苹果公司被解雇可能是发生在我身上的最好的事情了，而当时的我并没有看到这一点。我卸下成功者的沉重负担，重新成为一个轻松的创业者，对一切都不再那么肯定。这让我感觉如此自由，从而进入了人生中最富有创造力的时期之一。

在接下来的 5 年里，我开了一家叫做 NeXT 的公司，又开一家叫做皮克斯的公司，也爱上了一个了不起的女人。这个女人后来成了我的妻子。皮克斯公司制作了世界上第一部电脑动画电影《玩具总动员》，现在它是世界上最成功的动画工作室。在大规模的购并中，苹果公司收购了 NeXT，于是我又回到了苹果。我们在 NeXT 研发出的技术成为后来苹果复兴的核心技术。我和劳伦也拥有了美满的家庭，幸福地生活在一起。

如果当初我不被苹果解雇，我敢肯定这一切将不可能发生。这帖药很苦，但是我想病人很需要它。有时生活会给你迎头一击，但不要失去信心。我确信唯一让我一直走下去的，就是我对自己事业的热爱。你得找到你的至爱，无论工作，还是爱情，都应如此。

我的第三个故事是关于死亡的。我 17 岁时读到一句名言，大概是这样说的："如果你把每一天当成最后一天去过，那么终有一天你肯定是正确

certainly be right." It made an impression on me, and since then, for the past 33 years, I have looked in the mirror every morning and asked myself: "If today were the last day of my life, would I want to do what I am about to do today?" And whenever the answer has been "No" for too many days in a row, I know I need to change something.

Remembering that I'll be dead soon is the most important tool I've ever encountered to help me make the big choices in life. Because almost everything—all external expectations, all pride, all fear of embarrassment or failure—these things just fall away in the face of death, leaving only what is truly important.

About a year ago I was diagnosed with cancer. I had a scan at 7:30 in the morning. It clearly showed a tumor on my **pancreas**[①]. I didn't even know what a pancreas was. The doctors told me this was almost certainly a type of cancer that is incurable, and that I should expect to live no longer than three to six months. My doctor advised me to go home and get my affairs in order, which is doctor's code for prepare to die.

I lived with that diagnosis all day. Later that evening I had a biopsy, where they stuck an endoscope down my throat, through my stomach and into my **intestines**[②], put a needle into my pancreas and got a few cells from the tumor. When they viewed the cells under a microscope the doctors started crying because it turned out to be a very rare form of pancreatic cancer that is curable with surgery. I had the surgery and I'm fine now. This was the closest I've been

① pancreas ['pæŋkriəs] n. 胰脏

② intestine [in'testin] n. 肠

的。”这让我印象深刻。从那以后，在过去的33年里，我每天早上看着镜子中的自己，扪心自问：“如果今天是我生命中的最后一天，我还要做今天本来要去做的事情吗？”每当连续几天答案都是“不”时，我就知道我需要改变了。

时刻提醒自己终将死去，是我遇到的最重要的“工具”，它能帮助我做出人生的重大抉择。因为几乎所有的东西——所有外部期望、所有的骄傲、所有对难堪或失败的恐惧——面对死亡时，这些东西便灰飞烟灭了，只留下真正重要的东西。

大约一年前，我被诊断出患了癌症。我在早上7点半作了断层扫描，结果清楚地显示我的胰腺上有一个肿瘤。我甚至都不知道胰腺是什么东西。医生们告诉我，这几乎是一种无法治愈的癌症，我存活的时间大概不超过三到六个月。医生建议我回家，把诸事安排妥当，这是医生让我准备后事的暗语。

我整天都想着那个诊断结果。那天晚上我做了一个活切片检查。他们将一个内窥镜伸进我的喉咙，穿过我的胃，进入我的肠子，用一根针在我的胰腺肿瘤上取了几个细胞。当他们在显微镜下观察那些细胞后，医生开始哭泣，因为那是一个非常罕见的胰腺癌，通过手术是可以治愈的。我做了这个手术，现在我痊愈了。这是我最近距离面对死亡的经历。有过这样的经历，我现在可以更确定地谈论死亡，而不仅仅把它当成一个有用的纯粹的理论概念。

to facing death. Having lived through it, I can now talk about it with a bit more certainty than when death was a useful but purely intellectual concept.

Death is very likely the single best invention of Life. It is Life's change agent. It clears out the old to make way for the new. Your time is limited, so don't waste it living someone else's life. Don't be trapped by **dogma**[①]—which is living with the results of other people's thinking. Don't let the noise of others' opinions drown out your own inner voice. And most important, have the courage to follow your heart and intuition. They somehow already know what you truly want to become. Everything else is secondary.

① dogma ['dɔ:gmə,'dɔgmə] n. 教条；教义；信条

死亡很可能是生命最好的发明。它是推动生命改变的催化剂。它将旧的生命清除以便给新的生命让路。你的时间是有限的，所以不要浪费时间去过别人的生活。不要被教条束缚住手脚——盲从教条就是活在别人思考的结果里。不要被其他人喧嚣的观点掩盖住你内心真实的声音。最重要的是，要有勇气去跟随你的内心和直觉，只有它们知道你真正想成为什么。其他一切都是次要的。

I Never Write Right
小女孩的作家梦

◎ Linda Stafford

When I was fifteen, I announced to my English class that I was going to write and **illustrate**[①] my own books. Half the students **sneered**[②], the rest nearly fell out of their chairs laughing. "Don't be silly, only geniuses can become writers," the English teacher said smugly, "And you are getting a D this semester." I was so humiliated I burst into tears.

That night I wrote a short sad poem about broken dreams and mailed it to the Capri's Weekly newspaper. To my astonishment, they published it and sent me two dollars. I was a published and paid writer. I showed my teacher and fellow students. They laughed. "Just plain dumb luck," the teacher said. I tasted success. I'd sold the first thing I'd ever written. That was more than any of them had done and if it was just dumb luck, that was fine with me.

During the next two years I sold dozens of poems, letters, jokes and recipes. By the time I graduated from high school, with a C minus average, I had

① illustrate ['iləstreit] v. 举例说明；（为书）作插图，图解

② sneer [sniə] v. 嘲笑，冷笑

在我 15 岁的时候，我在英语课上宣布：我要编写我自己的书，并为之设计插画。一半的学生开始窃笑，其余的则笑得几乎从椅子上跌下来。“别傻了，只有天才才能成为作家，”英文老师自以为是地说道，“而你这个学期的成绩只是‘差’。”我感觉受到了奇耻大辱，忍不住放声大哭起来。

那天晚上，我写了一首关于梦想破灭的伤心短诗，并将它寄给了《卡普里周报》。令我惊讶的是，他们发表了它，并给我寄来了 2 美元稿酬。我成了一个发表过作品并取得了稿费的作家。我把那首诗拿给老师和同学看，他们笑了。“瞎猫逮着死耗子。”老师说道。我尝到了成功的甜蜜，我卖掉了我所写的第一篇作品。那是他们任何人未能做到的，就算只是因为运气，我也无所谓。

在接下来的两年里，我发表了几十篇诗歌、书信、笑话和食谱。从高中毕业时我的平均成绩只有“中”，但是我的剪贴簿里已经贴满了我发表的作品。我从来没有向我的老师、朋友或家人再次提起我的写作，因为他们

scrapbooks filled with my published work. I never mentioned my writing to my teachers, friends or my family again. They were dream killers and if people must choose between their friends and their dreams, they must always choose their dreams.

I had four children at the time, and the oldest was only four. While the children napped, I typed on my ancient typewriter. I wrote what I felt. It took nine months, just like a baby. I chose a publisher at random and put the **manuscript**[①] in an empty Pampers diapers package, the only box I could find. I'd never heard of manuscript boxes. The letter I enclosed read, "I wrote this book myself, I hope you like it. I also do the illustrations. Chapter six and twelve are my favourites. Thank you." I tied a string around the diaper box and mailed it without a self addressed stamped envelope and without making a copy of the manuscript.

A month later I received a contract, an advance on royalties, and a request to start working on another book. Crying Wind, the title of my book, became a best seller, was translated into fifteen languages and Braille and sold worldwide. I appeared on TV talk shows during the day and changed diapers at night. I traveled from New York to California and Canada on promotional tours. My first book also became required reading in native American schools in Canada.

The worst year I ever had as a writer I earned two dollars. I was fifteen, remember? In my best year I earned 36,000 dollars. Most years I earned between five thousand and ten thousand. No, it isn't enough to live on, but it's still more than I'd make working part time and it's five thousand to ten thousand more than I'd make if I didn't write at all. People ask what college I attended,

---

① manuscript ['mænjuskript] n. 手稿；原稿

是梦想杀手。如果有人要在朋友和梦想之间作出选择，他们总应该选择后者。

我有四个孩子，最大的那时只有 4 岁。孩子们进入梦乡时，我就开始在那台老掉牙的打字机上敲入文字。我花了整整九个月时间写下自己的感受，这部书稿就像是一个婴儿，而我就像是一位怀胎十月的母亲。然后，我随意选择了一家出版社，将手稿用空的“帮宝适”尿布盒子包起来——这是我唯一能找到的盒子了。我从来没听说过什么手稿箱。在随手稿附上的信里，我写道："这本书是我自己写的，希望你喜欢它。插图也是我自己画的。第六章和第十二章是我的最爱。谢谢。”我用绳子捆好尿布盒子，然后寄了出去，没有在信封上写上自己的地址，甚至也没有留下一份手稿的复印件。

一个月后，我收到一份合同、一份预付款，以及一份让我着手写另一本书的请求。我的书《哭泣的风》成了畅销书，并被译成 15 国文字和盲文销往世界各地。我白天出现在电视访谈节目中，晚上则回家换尿片。我从纽约来到加州、加拿大巡回宣传我的书。我的第一本书也被列入加拿大美国本土学校的必读书目。

我作为一个作家，最糟糕的一年只挣到了 2 美元，那年我 15 岁，还记得吗？而我干得最好的时候，一年可以挣 36,000 美元。大多数时候，我的收入在 5,000 至 10,000 之间。依靠这些钱过日子是远远不够的，但它仍然超过我做兼职工作的收入，而且如果我没有写作，那我连这每年 5,000

what degrees I had and what qualifications I have to be a writer. The answer is: "None." I just write. I'm not a genius. I'm not gifted and I don't write right. I'm lazy, undisciplined, and spend more time with my children and friends than I do writing. I didn't own a thesaurus until four years ago and I use a small Webster's dictionary that I'd bought at K-Mart for 89 cents. I use an electric typewriter that I paid a hundred and twenty nine dollars for six years ago. I've never used a word processor. I do all the cooking, cleaning and laundry for a family of six and fit my writing in a few minutes here and there. I write everything in longhand on yellow tablets while sitting on the sofa with my four kids eating pizza and watching TV. When the book is finished, I type it and mail it to the publisher. I've written eight books. Four have been published and three are still out with the publishers. One stinks. To all those who dream of writing, I'm shouting at you: "Yes, you can. Yes, you can. Don't listen to them." I don't write right but I've beaten the **odds**[①]. Writing is easy, it's fun and anyone can do it. Of course, a little dumb luck doesn't hurt.

① odds [ɔdz] n. 机率，可能性；差别；让步；优势

到 10,000 的收入也不会有。人们常常问我读了什么大学、获得了什么学位和资格才成为一个作家。我的答案是："什么也没有。"我只是写作。我并不是一个天才，没有天赋才华，甚至不能正确地书写。我很懒惰，没有经过任何正式训练；比起花在写作上的时间，我在孩子和朋友身上花去更多的时间。直到四年前，我才有了一本同义词典，之前一直用的是在凯马特超市用 89 美分买的韦氏袖珍词典。我用的是六年前花 129 美元买的电动打字机，从来不用文字处理程序。我要为我的六口之家洗衣、做饭、打扫卫生，有空的时候，见缝插针地这里写几分钟，那里写几分钟。陪四个孩子坐在沙发上一边吃比萨饼一边看电视时，我总是把想到的东西快速地记在黄色的笔记簿上。这本书完成后，我把它打印出来邮寄给出版商。我一共写了八本书，四本已出版，三本还在出版社。还有一本糟透了。对于那些梦想写作的人，我想大喊一声："没错，你可以的。是的，你一定行。别听他们的。"虽然我不能正确书写，但是我战胜了困难，实现了原本不可能的梦想。写作很容易，而且十分有趣，每个人都可以写作。当然，有点好运气并没什么害处。

Chapter 4

浮生若梦的幻影

Imagination is more important than knowledge. Knowledge is limited. Imagination encircles the world.

想象力比知识更为重要。知识是有限的，而想象力则包围着整个世界。

A Haunted House

鬼屋

◎ Virginia Woolf

Whatever hour you woke there was a door shutting. From room to room they went, hand in hand, lifting here, opening there, making sure—a ghostly couple.

"Here we left it," she said. And he added, "Oh, but here too." "It's upstairs," she murmured. "And in the garden," he whispered. "Quietly," they said, "or we shall wake them."

But it wasn't that you woke us. Oh, no. "They're looking for it; they're drawing the curtain," one might say, and so read on a page or two. "Now they've found it," one would be certain, stopping the pencil on the margin. And then, tired of reading, one might rise and see for oneself, the house all empty, the doors standing open, only the wood pigeons bubbling with content and the hum of the threshing machine sounding from the farm. "What did I come in here for? What did I want to find?" My hands were empty. "Perhaps it's upstairs then?" The apples were in the loft. And so down again, the garden still as ever, only the book had slipped into the grass.

作者小课堂

弗吉尼亚·伍尔夫（Virginia Woolf，1882—1941），英国女作家、批判家，意识流小说的代表人物之一。20 世纪现代主义与女性主义的先锋，成立了名叫布鲁姆斯伯利派的文学社团。代表作有《戴洛维夫人》《灯塔行》《雅各的房间》等。

无论什么时候醒来，总会听到关门的声音。于是他们手拉着手，逐间屋子仔细检查，一一确认——是一对鬼夫妻。

“还剩这间。”她说。“噢，这儿也是……”他补充道。“在楼上。”她嘟哝了一句。“花园里也有。”他悄声说。“小声点儿，否则会吵醒他们。”他们同时开口。

但其实不是你们吵醒了我们。哦，不，“他们正在努力寻找着；他们在窗帘上画着什么。”其中一个说道，然后读了一两页。“现在他们找到了。”其中一人非常确定地边说边停下了手里的铅笔。然后，他们观察得累了，一人自顾自地起身去查看。房子空空如也，门也都静静地敞开着，只有斑鸠咕咕的声音和远处农场打谷机传来的嗡嗡声。“我刚刚是进来干什么来的？我是想找到什么？”我的手里什么东西也没有。“也许是在楼上？”突然想到是否是阁楼上的苹果滚动的声音。但是又一无所获地下来了，花园

But they had found it in the drawing room. Not that one could ever see them. The windowpanes reflected apples, reflected roses; all the leaves were green in the glass. If they moved in the drawing room, the apple only turned its yellow side. Yet, the moment after, if the door was opened, spread about the floor, hung upon the walls, pendant from the ceiling—what? My hands were empty. The shadow of a thrush crossed the carpet; from the deepest wells of silence the wood pigeon drew its bubble of sound. "Safe, safe, safe" the pulse of the house beat softly. "The treasure buried; the room…" the pulse stopped short. Oh, was that the buried treasure?

A moment later the light had faded. Out in the garden then? But the trees spun darkness for a wandering beam of sun. So fine, so rare, coolly sunk beneath the surface the beam I sought always burned behind the glass. Death was the glass; death was between us, coming to the woman first, hundreds of years ago, leaving the house, sealing all the windows; the rooms were darkened. He left it, left her, went North, went East, saw the stars turned in the Southern sky; sought the house, found it dropped beneath the Downs. "Safe, safe, safe," the pulse of the house beat gladly. "The Treasure yours."

The wind roars up the avenue. Trees stoop and bend this way and that. Moonbeams splash and spill wildly in the rain. But the beam of the lamp falls straight from the window. The candle burns stiff and still. Wandering through the house, opening the windows, whispering not to wake us, the ghostly couple seek their joy.

"Here we slept," she says. And he adds, "Kisses without number." "Waking in the morning—" "Silver between the trees—" "Upstairs—" "In the garden—"

也安静如初，只有书本滑落到草地上的痕迹。

但他们又在客厅找到了什么。不是他们亲眼看到了什么，而是玻璃窗反射出苹果和玫瑰的影子；从玻璃里透过的树叶都是绿茵茵的。如果鬼魅在客厅中移动，那苹果只会映射出泛黄的那一面。但是紧接着，如果门是开着的，那么那些散落在地上、贴挂在墙面、悬挂在天花板上的……什么？我手里竟然还是空空如也。一只画眉的身影跃过地毯；斑鸠从静寂深井里发出冒泡的声音，“安了，安了，安了……”这座房子拍打着轻柔的节奏。“难道这房间下有埋藏的宝藏……”节奏骤然停止。噢，真的是埋藏的宝藏吗？

过了一会儿，灯光渐暗。花园里又是怎样一番景象呢？树木透过黑暗，跳跃在一束阳光里。如此精妙，如此罕见，那些我追寻的光束总是看似静谧地沉浸在表面，殊不知玻璃已被深深地灼热。这就是玻璃之死；死亡就在你我之间，从数千年前的女人开始，弃掉这座房子，密封所有的窗户，每个房间都笼罩在黑暗里。随着南方的天空星现星陨，他离开了这里，离开了她，去了北方，去了东部，任凭这屋子在开阔的高地中慢慢被湮没……“安了，安了，安了……”屋子的节奏又轻快地敲打起来。“原来这就是你们所寻求的宝藏。”

风顺着林荫道呼啸而来，树被吹得东倒西歪。月光倾泻而下，肆意飞舞在雨中。但是灯光却直直地从窗户透了出来，烛火忽明忽暗地燃烧着。游走在这所屋子的每个角落，轻轻推开所有的窗户，那些不会打扰到我们的悄悄话，都是这对鬼夫妻寻觅着的小愉悦。

“或许我们该睡了。”她说。“无数的亲吻。”他补充道。“当清晨醒

"When summer came—" "In winter snowtime—" The doors go shutting far in the distance, gently knocking like the pulse of a heart.

Nearer they come, cease at the doorway. The wind falls, the rain slides silver down the glass. Our eyes darken, we hear no steps beside us; we see no lady spread her ghostly cloak. His hands shield the lantern. "Look," he breathes. "Sound asleep. Love upon their lips."

Stooping, holding their silver lamp above us, long they look and deeply. Long they pause. The wind drives straightly; the flame stoops slightly. Wild beams of moonlight cross both floor and wall, and, meeting, stain the faces bent; the faces pondering; the faces that search the sleepers and seek their hidden joy.

"Safe, safe, safe," the heart of the house beats proudly. "Long years—" he sighs. "Again you found me." "Here," she murmurs, "sleeping; in the garden reading; laughing, rolling apples in the loft. Here we left our treasure—" Stooping, their light lifts the lids upon my eyes. "Safe! Safe! Safe!" the pulse of the house beats wildly. Waking, I cry "Oh, is this your buried treasure? The light in the heart."

来——”“当银色洒满树林——”“当楼上——”“当花园里——”“当盛夏来临——”“当雪中穿梭——”远远的，门被合上了，只剩下轻柔的敲门声如同心脏的蠢蠢跳动融化在空气里。

他们越走越近，在门口停下脚步。风轻轻地掠过，雨水泛着银色的光亮顺着玻璃窗滑落。我们眼前一黑，听不到身旁的脚步声；也没有看到穿着黑色斗篷如鬼魅般的女子。他的手持着油灯。“看！”他的呼吸声匀促有力。“听起来像是睡着了，愿爱停留在他们的唇齿之间。”

他们弯腰将银色灯盏举过头顶，意味深长地打量着，停驻了许久。风直直地呼啸而过，火苗也被吹弯了腰。窗外的月光放肆地浸透着每一寸地板和墙壁，交相辉映，像足了一张张扭曲的、深思的和试图探索沉睡者隐藏的快乐的脸。

“安了，安了，安了……”如心脏般的律动再次高昂响起。“许多年——”他哼了起来，“你再次寻到了我。”“就在这里，”她轻声接唱，“安睡着；我们在花园里理解着世界，笑着，在阁楼上滚动苹果。这都是我们曾丢弃掉的财富——”弯下身，却有光明为我揭开欣赏世界的眼帘。“安了！安了！安了！”游荡在这座房子的律动越鸣越野。梦醒，我哭了，“噢，这就是被掩埋了的财富？那可以照亮心间的光芒！”

The Black Cat
黑猫

◎ Edgar Allan Poe

I know you will not believe this story. Only a madman could hope that you would believe it—and I am not mad. But as I am going to die tomorrow, I would like to tell my story to the world today. Perhaps some day, somebody more calm and less excitable than me, will be able to explain it.

I have always loved animals. I loved them deeply, from the very first days of my life. When I was young, we always had many animals in our house, and so I used to spend most of my days playing with them and taking care of them. As the years passed, I grew into a quiet, gentle man, and my love for animals grew too. I found that they were more friendly, more honest than most men Animals were always my best friends.

I got married when I was quite young. Luckily, my wife loved animals too, and she used to buy me many animals as presents. In fact, our house was always full of animals—we had birds, fish, a dog, chickens, and a cat.

This cat, whom we called Pluto, was a large black cat. He was a beautiful animal, and he was also very clever. I loved Pluto more than I loved all my other

作者小课堂

埃德加·爱伦·坡（Edgar Allan Poe，1809—1849），19世纪美国诗人、小说家和文学评论家，和马克·吐温齐名。其文风诡异，崇尚神秘主义，被誉为侦探小说的鼻祖。作品是在任何时代都是“独一无二”的风格。代表作《怪诞故事集》《黑猫》《莫格街谋杀案》等。

我知道你们不会信这个故事。只有疯子才会指望你们相信它的真实——我又没疯。但是鉴于明天就是我的死期，我今天还是要把我的故事说出来。或许今后某些比我明察秋毫的人，会解释这一切蹊跷。

我一降生就喜欢动物，可以说是非常爱。小时候，家里有很多动物，我总是一天到晚跟它们泡在一起，并负责照顾它们。随着时光流逝，我长成一位安静内敛的绅士，而我对动物的感情也与日俱增。我越发觉得它们的友好和忠诚了，其中大部分的雄性动物都是我最好的朋友。

我很早就结婚了。幸运的是，我的妻子也很爱动物，她常常买些动物当做礼物送给我。实际上，我们家简直就是个汇集了鸟、鱼、狗、鸡、猫的动物园。

我们有一只大黑猫，叫布鲁托。它真是漂亮极了，还很聪明。在我的动物们中，我最爱的就是布鲁托。我想亲自为他操办一切事情，所以从不

animals. I wanted to do everything for him myself, so I never let my wife take care of him. I used to play with him and give him his food, and he followed me everywhere I went.

For several years Pluto and I were the best of friends, but during this time my life slowly changed. I became a heavy drinker, and my need for alcohol soon grew into a terrible disease. I was often angry and violent. I began to shout at my wife, and I even started to hit her. My animals, too, felt the change in me. I stopped taking care of them and sometimes I was even cruel to them. But I was never cruel to Pluto. As time passed, my disease grew worse, and soon even Pluto was not safe from my violence.

One night I arrived home late. I was very, very drunk. When Pluto saw me, he tried to run away from me, and this made me angry. I caught him by his neck and shook him. He, in his fright, bit me on the hand. At once, a wild, terrible anger filled me, and I could feel nothing except burning hate. Slowly I took a knife from my pocket, opened it, and then carefully cut out one of Pluto's eyes from its socket. I shake today as I write these words down. Every time I remember that day, I still feel sadness and pain.

When I woke up the next morning, I felt ashamed of what I had done. But this feeling was not strong enough to make me change my life. I continued to drink because it was too difficult for me to stop. Soon, I had forgotten what I had done.

As the months passed, Pluto got better. His empty eye socket still looked terrible, but at least he wasn't in pain any more. Not surprisingly, he used to run away from me when he saw me, frightened that I would hurt him again. At first

让妻子插手来照顾他。我经常和它玩耍，给它喂食，它也总是天天屁颠颠地围着我转。

布鲁托和我成了相伴多年的好朋友，可是我的生活也在悄悄起着变化。我变成了一个酒鬼，我嗜酒的程度之深以至于让我患了重病，从此变得易怒和暴力。我开始冲妻子发火，甚至动手打她。我的动物们，也同样感受到了我的变化。我不再好好照顾它们，有时候甚至以虐待它们为乐，当然，布鲁托除外，我从不动它。随着时间的推移，我的病情恶化了，最近连布鲁托也未能幸免于难，成了我施暴的对象。

有一天我喝得酩酊大醉，很晚才回到家。布鲁托看到我，试图赶紧逃开，这让我火冒三丈。我掐住它的脖子用力摇晃。它带着巨大的恐惧咬伤了我的手。顿时，一股强烈的怒火涌遍我全身，就如正在熊熊燃烧的仇恨。我慢慢地从口袋里掏出一把弹簧刀，一点一点地，把布鲁托的一只眼球从眼眶里挖了出来。直到现在写下这些文字，我的身体仍然止不住地颤抖。每次想起当时的情景，我仍然会被笼罩在难以言喻的悲伤和痛苦之中。

第二天早上起床后，我为昨晚的事羞愧难当。可这种感觉还是没强烈到足以让我改变当时的生活。我仍然嗜酒如命，酒这玩意儿真是太诱惑人了。很快，我甚至忘了自己曾造过的孽。

几个月后，布鲁托恢复了许多。它空洞洞的眼眶看上去还是挺吓人的，

I was sad to see him run away—an animal which had once so loved me. Then I began to feel a little angry. There is something strange about the human heart. We humans seem to like hurt-ing ourselves. Haven't we all, a hundred times, done something stupid or evil just because we know that we should not do it? It was because of this, this need to hurt myself, that I did this next evil thing…

One morning I woke, found a rope and calmly tied it round Pluto's neck. Then I hung the poor animal from a tree and left it there to die. I cried as I did this terrible thing. My face was wet with tears and my heart was black and heavy. But I killed it. I killed it because I knew it had loved me, because it hadn't hurt me, even because I knew that I was doing something terrible and wrong.

That same night we had a fire in our house. I was woken from my sleep by loud shouts of "Fire!" When I opened my eyes, I found that the fire had already reached the bedroom. My wife and I ran out of the house as fast as we could. Luckily we escaped death, but the house and almost everything in it was destroyed.

The next day I went back into the house and saw several people standing in a group, looking at a wall. It was the only wall of the house that was still standing after the fire. It was one of my bedroom walls, the one where the head of my bed had rested. As I came nearer to the wall I heard someone say, "How strange!" and another person, "That's impossible!" And then I saw it—a huge cat. Not a real cat, but the shape of a cat outlined in the white bedroom wall. It was as clear as a picture. I could even see a rope around the animal's neck.

I stood there in horror, too frightened to move. Then, slowly, I thought back to the night before. I had left the cat hanging from a tree, in the garden at

但是好歹它不觉得痛了。不出所料，它一看到我就跑得很远，生怕我会再次伤害它。起初，看到这个曾经跟我很亲密的小东西如今再也不愿和我亲近，心里还是十分难过。后来，我开始觉得有点恼人。人心就是蹊跷。我们人类似乎也喜欢自我折磨。可是，总有那么多人，一遍又一遍地做着本不愿做、却又无法控制的糊涂事。就是这种观念作祟，这种自我折磨的潜在需求，让我又做了一件错事。

一天早上，我醒来后看到了一根绳子，就随意地往布鲁托的脖子上绕了绕。然后我把这个可怜的小东西挂到一棵树上，就这样让它慢慢等死。我为自己这种龌龊的行径流泪了。泪流满面的我，感到自己心狠手辣，又心情沉重。但我却杀了它，或许因为它曾经很黏我，或许因为它并未伤害过我，甚至因为我深知自己的恶性，所以我得杀了它。

就在那晚，我在房间里生火取暖。可后来我却被一阵尖叫声吵醒："起火啦！"我睁开眼睛，发现火苗已经蹿到了我的卧室门口。我和妻子赶紧跑出了房子。所幸我们人无大碍，但是整座房子和里面的每一样东西都烧毁了。

第二天，我走近已经烧毁的房子，看到几个人站在一堆，正往一面墙上看着什么。这是火灾后唯一还没倒的一面墙，刚好是我房间靠床头的的那面墙。当我离墙越来越近时，听到有人在说："真是奇怪！"另外有一个人说："这，不可能的吧！"最后我看到了——一只巨大的猫。不是真猫，而是卧室这面白墙上留下的一个猫的形状，它就如一幅画一样清晰。我甚

the back of my house. When a neighbour had first noticed the fire, many people had run into the garden. One of them had probably cut the cat from the tree and thrown it through my open window, in order to wake me up. The cat's body had hit my bedroom wall and left its shape there, because the plaster on that wall was new and still soft.

Although I thought that this was a very reasonable explanation, the strange shape on the wall still worried me. I thought about the cat day and night. I began to feel sorry that I had killed it. I started walking around the streets at night looking at all the cats, to see if I could find another one like Pluto.

One night, I was drinking in my favourite bar when I suddenly noticed a large, black cat. I went up to it and touched it. It was very large—as large as Pluto had been. It also looked very like Pluto. Except for one thing. Pluto had been black all over, but this cat had a white mark on its front.

I touched the cat and he immediately lay down against my leg and seemed very friendly towards me. This, I decided, was the cat that I wanted. I offered the barman some money to buy the cat from him, but he said that the cat didn't belong to him. In fact, he had no idea where it had come from.

So I took the cat home. My wife liked it immediately, and it stayed with us from that day. But soon—I do not know why—the cat started to make me angry, and, as time passed, I began to hate it. I did not hurt it in any way, but I always tried to keep as far away from it as possible.

I knew one reason why I hated this cat so much. On the morning after I had brought it home, I saw that, like Pluto, it had lost one of its eyes. My wife, who was the kind, gentle person that I had once been, only loved the cat more because

至能看到猫脖子上绕着的那根绳子。

我呆若木鸡，诚惶诚恐地站在那儿不敢动。接着，我渐渐地回想起了那晚的情形——我将布鲁托吊在房屋后花园的树上。当邻居刚发现起火的时候，很多人都跑进了花园。有人割断了吊着布鲁托的绳子，把它从其中一扇开着的窗户扔了进来，想以此来叫醒我。布鲁托用身子不断撞击着我卧室的墙，所以那面又软又掉壁灰的新墙留下了它身体的形状。

虽然我认为这是一个很合理的解释，但是墙上奇怪的图形还是让我心惊胆颤。我开始对布鲁托日思夜想，并为我对它所下的毒手而深感愧疚。我开始在夜间走上街头，观察所有的猫，希望找到另一只和布鲁托很像的猫。

一天晚上，我正在常去的酒吧里喝酒，突然看到了一只很大的黑猫。我赶紧朝它走去，轻轻抚摸着它。它的体型跟布鲁托一样大，长得也很像布鲁托。唯有一点例外。布鲁托全身都是黑色的，这只猫的前胸上有一小撮白色的毛。

我抚摸着这只猫，它也立即很友好地靠着我的腿趴了下来。这就是我想要的那只猫。我向酒吧老板提出花钱把这只猫买下，可他说猫不是他的。实际上，他也不知道这只猫是从哪儿蹿出来的。

于是，我便带着猫回家了。妻子立马看中了这个家伙，从那天起，它就跟我们相处在了一起。然而，很快地，不知为何这只猫就开始让我火大，而且我越来越讨厌它。尽管我没有伤害它，但总是试图离它远点。

of this. But the cat didn't like my wife. It loved me alone.

Every time I sat down, it used to jump onto my knees. When I went out of a room, it used to run out in front of me and get between my feet, or climb up my legs. At these times, I wanted to kill it. But I didn't, because I was too afraid—afraid of the cat, and even more afraid of the white mark on its chest.

I have already mentioned this mark. At first, there was nothing strange about it. It was just a white mark. But slowly this mark grew and changed until it had the clear shape of a terrible, a horrible thing—It was the shape of the gallows! Yes, those horrible wooden posts from which they hang men by a rope around the neck!

As each day passed, my fear grew and grew. I, a man, a strong man, had become afraid of a cat! Why was I so frightened, so worried by a stupid animal? Day and night, I could get no rest. I had the most terrible dreams, and my mind turned to dark, evil thoughts. I hated everything, everybody—and life itself.

One day my wife and I needed to get something from the cellar underneath the house. The cat followed us down the steps and threw itself in front of me. I almost fell on my face and, mad with anger, I took hold of an axe and tried to kill the animal. But my wife caught my arm to stop me, and then anger exploded in my mind. I turned and drove the axe deep into her head. She fell dead on the floor, without a sound.

After this horrible murder, I calmly made plans to hide the body. I knew I couldn't take it out of the house, either by day or night, because the neighbours would see me. So I had to think of other ways…I could cut the body up into very small pieces and then burn them in a fire. I could hide the body under the floor.

我心里其实很清楚自己为什么如此讨厌它。就在我带它回家的第二天早上，我竟然看见它跟布鲁托一样，也是没了一只眼睛！而我的妻子，这位似我以前那样温文尔雅的人，却对这只猫情有独钟。可是猫却不亲近我的妻子，它只喜欢我一个人。

每当我坐下来，它就跳上我的膝盖来。当我走出房间，它也喜欢跑到我前面，在我双脚之间钻来钻去，或者爬到我腿上。每每这时，我真是想杀了它。但是，我没有，我实在是太、太害怕猫了，尤其是它前胸上那撮标志性的白毛。

我上文提到过这撮白毛。起初这倒没什么奇怪的，就是一个白色的标记。然而这些毛发渐渐、渐渐地，长得越来越清晰，最后形成了一个可怕恐怖的东西，将我内心深处最害怕的东西给挖了出来——白毛长成了一个绞刑架的形状！是的，就是将人用绳子缠住脖子后，吊上去的那种恐怖木桩！

我的恐惧与日俱增。我，一个男人，一个强壮的男人，竟然变得怕猫！我怎么就这么怕这种傻动物呢？每日每夜，我心中的恐惧都闲不下来。我天天做噩梦，心理也变得十分阴暗邪恶。我厌倦所有的人和事，甚至厌倦了生活。

一天，我和妻子去地窖取东西。猫跟着我们下了台阶，突然间蹿到我前面，害我差点摔了个面朝天。我恼怒极了，提起斧头就准备杀了这畜生。而妻子抓住我的手臂阻止了这次杀戮，更是让我怒不可遏。我转身抬手一斧，深深地砍在妻子的头上。她当时就一声不吭地倒地断气了。

Or I could put the body in a box and then ask someone to carry the box away... Finally, I thought of a better idea. I decided to hide the body behind the walls of the cellar.

I knew immediately which wall to choose. There was a wall in the cellar round the bottom of an old chimney, which was no longer used. This wall had bricks in the front and back but was empty in the middle. I started work at once. I took out some of the bricks from the front wall and carefully put the body against the back wall. Then I put back the bricks and covered them with plaster. I made sure that the plaster did not look new, and soon the wall looked just the same as all the other walls. When I had finished my work, I looked at the plaster. "I've never done a better piece of work!" I said to myself happily.

I then looked around for the cat, to kill it. It had brought too much unhappiness into my life, and so it, too, must now die. I looked for it everywhere, but it had disappeared. I was free at last! That night I had a deep, peaceful sleep—I, who had just killed my wife, slept well!

Three days passed and still the cat did not appear. I was now a happy man, happier than I had been for a long time. I wasn't worried by what I had done. People had asked a few questions and the police had visited my house, but they had found nothing.

On the fourth day the police visited again and began to search the house. They looked into all the rooms and then went down into the cellar. I went with them, feeling calm and safe. I watched them as they looked everywhere. They seemed quite happy that there was nothing there and they got ready to leave. I was very happy. I was sure that I was safe, but I wanted to say something, just a

在这场残酷的杀戮后，我开始冷静下来，计划着该怎样藏匿尸体。我知道，无论白天还是夜晚，我都无法把尸体搬离屋子，因为肯定会被邻居看见。于是我得想点别的办法……我可以将尸体切成小块放在锅里给煮了。我可以把尸体埋在地板下。我也可以把尸体放在一个箱子里然后叫人把箱子运出去……最后，我想了一个更好的办法。我决定将尸体藏在地窖的墙皮里。

我很快就选好了藏尸的墙。地窖里靠近旧烟囱底部有一面不再用的墙，墙前后都砌了砖，但是中间是空的。我立马开动，准备凿墙藏尸。我先把前面的墙砖敲了一些下来，然后小心翼翼地将尸体竖着放了进去，然后将砖涂好石膏再砌回去。我看了下，石膏涂抹的部分看上去旧旧的，很快，这面墙看上去就和其他墙没什么区别了。搞定这一切后，我盯着这些石膏，开心地想："这真是我干得最漂亮的一件事儿！"

接着我开始找那只猫，准备把它也杀掉。它给我的生活带来了那么多不如意，它是该死！然而，我找遍整个屋子也找不到它。我终于解放啦！那晚，我睡得特别踏实——我这个刚刚杀了自己妻子的人，呵呵，竟然睡得如此安稳！

三天过去了，那只猫仍然没有现身。现在我可是一个快乐的人啦，比之前很长一段时间都要快乐。我也不再为自己造过的孽而担忧。左邻右舍也问过我几句，警察也检查过屋子，但是他们都一无所获。

第四天，警察又来了，开始搜查房间的每个角落。他们每间房都仔细地搜着，然后下到了地窖里。我也跟在后面，神情自若。他们搜地窖时，

word or two, to show how unworried I was.

"Gentlemen," I said, "I'm pleased that you've found nothing here, and that you are now leaving this hous...But let me show you something, gentlemen. Do you see how well built this house is? These walls, you will notice, are very strong."As I said these words, I knocked on the wall with a stick—the wall where I had hidden my wife!

At that moment we heard a sound. It was a strange sound, unlike anything I had ever heard before. The sound was soft at first, almost like a baby crying. Then it grew louder and louder and turned into one long, endless scream. It was like a cry rising from Hell.

The policemen looked at me, then at one another. They ran to the wall and started pulling out the bricks as fast as they could. In minutes the wall was down and there, for all to see, was the body of my dead wife. On top of her head, with a red, open mouth and one burning eye, sat the black cat—the animal which had made me a murderer, and which would now send me to my death.

I had put the horrible thing into the wall, alive, with my wife!

我就站在一边看。他们什么也没搜到，似乎开心地准备撤了。因为确保了自己没事，我也很高兴，但我还是想说两句什么，以示我高枕无忧。

“先生，”我说，“我很高兴你们没有在这儿发现什么，你们也正准备离开这房……但是先生们，我还想让你们知道个事，您有看到我这座房子很结实对吧？您会发现，这些墙都着实坚固。”我一边说着，一边用根棍子敲了敲那面藏有我妻子尸体的墙！

就在这一瞬间，我们都听到了一阵声响，奇怪的声响，跟我之前听到的任何声响都不一样。声音起初很柔和，就像婴儿在哭泣，而后越来越响，最后变成绵延凄厉的尖叫。听起来像是来自地狱般的哭嚎。

警察看着我，继而面面相觑。他们跑到墙边，开始一个劲儿地拆砖。仅几分钟工夫，墙就被拆掉了。所有人都看到了这一幕，我妻子的尸体就在里面。她张着的嘴还留有斑斑血迹，一只眼睛被灼瞎了，在她的头顶上，坐着一只黑色的猫——也就是它，让我成了一个凶手，现在，也将我送上了死亡之路。

我把这可怕的东西，活生生地，和我妻子一道埋进了墙里！

The Monkey's Paw (Ⅰ)
猴爪（1）

◎ W. W. Jacobs

"Be careful what you wish for, you may receive it."

—Anonymous

Without, the night was cold and wet, but in the small parlour of Laburnum villa the blinds were drawn and the fire burned brightly. Father and son were at chess; the former, who posessed ideas about the game involving radical chances, putting his king into such sharp and unnecessary perils that it even provoked comment from the white-haired old lady knitting placidly by the fire.

"Hark at the wind," said Mr. White, who, having seen a fatal mistake after it was too late, was amiably desirous of preventing his son from seeing it.

"I'm listening," said the latter grimly surveying the board as he streched out his hand. "Check."

"I should hardly think that he's come tonight," said his father, with his hand poised over the board.

作者小课堂

威廉·威马克·雅各布斯（W.W.Jacobs，1863—1943），英国著名小说家，生于伦敦，毕业于伯克拜克大学。他是一个多产的小说家，写过大量的讽刺小说和恐怖小说。这篇著于1901年的《猴爪》是他的主要代表作，曾被多次改编为电影和剧本，斯蒂芬·金的小说《宠物公墓》深受其影响。

“小心许愿，因为你不知道它将如何实现。”

——佚名

屋外，夜晚冰凉而湿润，但金链花别墅小客厅的百叶窗却开着，屋里透出明亮的炉火光。父亲和儿子在屋里下国际象棋；父亲认为这个游戏彻底靠运气，于是把国王置于不必要的险境，就连坐在壁炉边静静织毛衣的白发老妇人都忍不住惊呼起来。

“你听，外面的风声可真大。”怀特先生说。当他发现自己犯了致命错误，已成落地棋时，只好故作和善地希望儿子不要发现。

“我听到了。”儿子说。他面无表情地盯住棋盘，察看片刻，然后伸出一只手。“将！”

“他今晚大概不会来了。”父亲说着，手悬停在棋盘上方。

"Mate," replied the son.

"That's the worst of living so far out," bawled Mr. White with sudden and unlooked-for violence; "Of all the beastly, slushy, out of the way places to live in, this is the worst. Path's a bog, and the road's a torrent. I don't know what people are thinking about. I suppose because only two houses in the road are let, they think it doesn't matter."

"Never mind, dear," said his wife soothingly; "perhaps you'll win the next one."

Mr. White looked up sharply, just in time to intercept a knowing glance between mother and son. The words died away on his lips, and he hid a guilty grin in his thin grey beard.

"There he is," said Herbert White as the gate banged to loudly and heavy footsteps came toward the door.

The old man rose with hospitable haste and opening the door, was heard condoling with the new arrival. The new arrival also condoled with himself, so that Mrs. White said, "Tut, tut!" and coughed gently as her husband entered the room followed by a tall, burly man, beady of eye and rubicund of visage.

"Sergeant-Major Morris," he said, introducing him.

The Sergeant-Major took hands and taking the proffered seat by the fire, watched contentedly as his host got out whiskey and tumblers and stood a small copper kettle on the fire.

At the third glass his eyes got brighter, and he began to talk, the little family circle regarding with eager interest this visitor from distant parts, as he squared his broad shoulders in the chair and spoke of wild scenes and doughty deeds; of

“呵呵，将死啦！”儿子说。

“这是到目前为止最糟糕的生活环境，”怀特先生突然激动地高声抱怨起来，“在所有恶劣而泥泞的偏远住地中，这里是最糟糕的。小路如沼泽，大道像河沟。我真纳闷，人们究竟是怎么想的。我猜，由于这一带只有两间房可出租，所以人们也就不在乎了。”

“没关系，亲爱的，”妻子安慰他说，“说不定你下一盘能赢呢。”

怀特先生猛地抬起头，恰好看见母亲和儿子在互递眼色。他不好意思再说下去，灰白的胡子下面藏着一抹坏笑。

这时，有人砰地推开院门，迈着沉重的脚步走进屋来。“他来了。”赫伯特·怀特说。

好客的老头赶忙站起来，打开客厅门。随后，门口传来了他向客人致以问候的声音。客人还问起了他的近况，于是怀特太太轻呼“嘘，嘘”。丈夫进屋时，身后跟着一个高大健壮的男人，他眼睛明亮、面色红润，怀特太太轻咳了两声。

“这是莫里斯军士长。”怀特先生向家人介绍了这位来客。

莫里斯跟大家握了手，在主人在壁炉边给他准备好的椅子上坐了下来。他高兴地看着主人拿出威士忌和平底酒杯，又在壁炉架上摆出一把小铜壶。

第三杯酒下肚之后，莫里斯的眼睛变得闪闪发亮，开始跟大家交谈起来。一家人远远地望着这位客人，对他产生了浓厚的兴趣。莫里斯在椅子上耸起宽阔的双肩，讲述异国风光和他的英勇事迹，讲述战争、瘟疫和奇人异事。

wars and plagues and strange peoples.

"Twenty-one years of it," said Mr. White, nodding at his wife and son. "When he went away he was a slip of a youth in the warehouse. Now look at him."

"He don't look to have taken much harm." said Mrs. White politely.

"I'd like to go to India myself," said the old man, "just to look around a bit, you know."

"Better where you are," said the Sergeant-Major, shaking his head. He put down the empty glass and sighning softly, shook it again.

"I should like to see those old temples and fakirs and jugglers," said the old man. "What was that that you started telling me the other day about a monkey's paw or something, Morris?"

"Nothing." said the soldier hastily. "Leastways, nothing worth hearing."

"Monkey's paw?" said Mrs. White curiously.

"Well, it's just a bit of what you might call magic, perhaps." said the Sargeant-Major off-handedly.

His three listeners leaned forward eagerly. The visitor absent-mindedly put his empty glass to his lips and then set it down again. His host filled it for him again.

"To look at," said the Sergeant-Major, fumbling in his pocket, "it's just an ordinary little paw, dried to a mummy."

He took something out of his pocket and proffered it. Mrs. White drew back with a grimace, but her son, taking it, examined it curiously.

"And what is there special about it?" inquired Mr. White as he took it from

“21 年前，”怀特先生对妻子和儿子点点头说，“他离开的时候，还是个瘦瘦的年轻仓货员。如今，再看看他。”

“现在的样子也没什么不好。”怀特太太礼貌地说。

“我也想去印度，”老头说，“你懂的，就想去那儿转一转。”

“还是在家更好。”莫里斯摇着头说。他放下空酒杯，轻叹一声，又摇了摇头。

“我很想瞧瞧那些老神庙、托钵僧和杂技演员。”老头说。“莫里斯，你是不是在前几天说过，要告诉我一件有关猴爪或别的什么东西的事吗，是什么呀？”

“没什么，”莫里斯赶紧说，“至少，也没什么好听的。”

“猴爪？”怀特太太好奇地凑过来。

“呃，那是个或许被你们称为魔幻的东西。”莫里斯立即回答。

三个听众迫不及待地探过身子想要听个究竟。客人茫然地把空酒杯举到唇边，随后又放下去。主人马上为他斟满了酒。

“瞧，”莫里斯一边说，一边在衣袋里摸索，“它就是个普通的小猴爪，只是被风干了。”

他从衣袋里掏出那个东西，举在手中。怀特太太厌恶地扭过头，她的儿子却把它接了过来，好奇地检查着。

“它有什么魔力？”怀特先生问。他从儿子手里拿过猴爪，打量片刻，随后把它放在桌子上。

“一个老僧人给它下了魔咒，”莫里斯说，“他是个非常神圣的人。他想

his son, and having examined it, placed it upon the table.

"It had a spell put on it by an old fakir," said the Sergeant-Major, "a very holy man. He wanted to show that fate ruled people's lifes, and that those who interefered with it did so to their sorrow. He put a spell on it so that three separate men could each have three wishes from it."

His manners were so impressive that his hearers were concious that their light laughter had jarred somewhat.

"Well, why don't you have three, sir?" said Herbert White cleverly.

The soldier regarded him the way that middle age is wont to regard presumptuous youth. "I have," he said quietly, and his blotchy face whitened.

"And did you really have the three wishes granted?" asked Mrs. White.

"I did," said the seargent-major, and his glass tapped against his strong teeth.

"And has anybody else wished?" persisted the old lady.

"The first man had his three wishes. Yes," was the reply, "I don't know what the first two were, but the third was for death. That's how I got the paw."

His tones were so grave that a hush fell upon the group.

"If you've had your three wishes it's no good to you now then Morris," said the old man at last. "What do you keep it for?"

The soldier shook his head. "Fancy I suppose," he said slowly. "I did have some idea of selling it, but I don't think I will. It has caused me enough mischief already. Besides, people won't buy. They think it's a fairy tale, some of them; and those who do think anything of it want to try it first and pay me afterward."

"If you could have another three wishes," said the old man, eyeing him

通过猴爪来证明人生全凭命运支配，凡是企图干预命运的人，都不会有好收场。他给这个猴爪下过魔咒之后，猴爪就可以分别满足三个人的愿望，但每人只能许三次愿。”

他的表情如此严肃认真，让这三位听众意识到他们的轻笑声让他感到不快。

“那么，先生，您为什么不许三个愿望呢？”赫伯特·怀特机灵地问道。

莫里斯盯着他。中年人打量不知天高地厚的小青年时，一般都爱用这种眼光。“我许了。”他平静地回答，布满斑痕的脸变得苍白起来。

“那你的三个愿望都实现了？”怀特太太问。

“是的。”莫里斯说，酒杯碰到他坚硬的牙齿，发出轻微的撞击声。

“还有人许过愿吗？”老妇人问道。

“嗯，第一个人也许了三个愿望，”莫里斯回答。“我不知道他的前两个愿望是什么，但他的第三个愿望是死亡。这就是我得到这个猴爪的原因。”

他的声音非常低沉，大家变得鸦雀无声。

“莫里斯，要是你许了三次愿，结果又对你没什么好处，”最后，老头说，“那你还留着它干什么呢？”

莫里斯摇摇头。“我估计，这大概是出于一种怪癖，”他慢慢地说。“我的确曾想把它卖掉，可我不会这么做。它已经给我带来够多的灾难了。再说，别人也不会买。一部分人以为它就是个童话故事；而那些多少有些相信的人想要先试一试，再付钱给我。”

keenly, "would you have them?"

"I don't know," said the other. "I don't know."

He took the paw, and dangling it between his forefinger and thumb, suddenly threw it upon the fire. White, with a slight cry, stooped down and snatched it off.

"Better let it burn," said the soldier solemnly.

"If you don't want it Morris," said the other, "give it to me."

"I won't." said his friend doggedly. "I threw it on the fire. If you keep it, don't blame me for what happens. Pitch it on the fire like a sensible man."

The other shook his head and examined his possesion closely. "How do you do it?" he inquired.

"Hold it up in your right hand, and wish aloud," said the sergeant-major, "But I warn you of the consequences."

"Sounds like the 'Arabian Nights'," said Mrs. White, as she rose and began to set the supper.

"Don't you think you might wish for four pairs of hands for me?"

Her husband drew the talisman from his pocket, and all three burst into laughter as the Seargent-Major, with a look of alarm on his face, caught him by the arm.

"If you must wish," he said gruffly, "Wish for something sensible."

Mr. White dropped it back in his pocket, and placing chairs, motioned his friend to the table. In the business of supper the talisman was partly forgotten, and afterward the three sat listening in an enthralled fashion to a second installment of the soldier's adventures in India.

“如果你还能许三个愿，”老头热切地盯着他，说道，“你还会许愿吗？”

“我不知道，”他说，“我不知道。”

莫里斯拿起猴爪，用食指和大拇指捏住它，摇晃几下，突然把它扔进壁炉里。怀特轻轻叫了一声，弯下腰，把猴爪取了出来。

“最好烧掉它。”莫里斯一脸严肃地说。

“莫里斯，如果你不想要它，”老头说，“就把它给我吧。”

“我不会给你的，”他的朋友坚决地说，“我要烧了它。要是你留着，以后发生什么事都不能怪我。若你够聪明的话，就该再把它扔进火里。”

老头赶紧摇头，仔细检查这新得到的宝贝。“你是怎么许愿的？”他问。

“举起右手，大声喊出你的愿望，”莫里斯说，“我要警告你，后果非常严重。”

“听起来像是《天方夜谭》。”怀特太太说着，站起身来，开始准备晚餐。

“你不觉得你该许个愿让我长出四双手来吗？”

丈夫从衣袋里拿出那个宝贝，三人开怀大笑。莫里斯惊慌地抓住老头的胳膊。

“假如你真想许愿，”他用沙哑的声音说，“最好说一些合情合理的愿望。”

怀特先生把猴爪放回衣袋，摆好椅子，让朋友坐到桌边来。吃晚饭时，三个人暂时忘记了那个宝贝，他们听莫里斯讲述印度冒险经历第二部，听

"If the tale about the monkey's paw is not more truthful than those he has been telling us," said Herbert, as the door closed behind their guest, just in time to catch the last train, "we shan't make much out of it."

"Did you give anything for it, father?" inquired Mrs. White, regarding her husband closely.

"A trifle," said he, colouring slightly, "He didn't want it, but I made him take it. And he pressed me again to throw it away."

"Likely," said Herbert, with pretended horror. "Why, we're going to be rich, and famous, and happy. Wish to be an emporer, father, to begin with; then you can't be henpecked."

He darted around the table, pursued by the maligned Mrs. White armed with an antimacassar.

Mr. White took the paw from his pocket and eyed it dubiously. "I don't know what to wish for, and that's a fact," he said slowly. "It seems to me I've got all I want."

"If you only cleared the house, you'd be quite happy, wouldn't you!" said Herbert, with his hand on his shoulder. "Well, wish for two hundred pounds, then; that'll just do it."

His father, smiling shamefacedly at his own credulity, held up the talisman, as his son, with a solemn face, somewhat marred by a wink at his mother, sat down and struck a few impressive chords.

"I wish for two hundred pounds," said the old man distinctly.

A fine crash from the piano greeted his words, interupted by a shuddering cry from the old man. His wife and son ran toward him.

得十分入迷。

“假如猴爪的故事和他告诉我们的其他故事一样不切实际，”当大门在客人身后关上时——他要去赶末班车，赫伯特说道，“我们也定然不能用它换到多少好处。”

“你给他报酬了吗，他爸？”怀特太太认真地看着丈夫问道。

“我给了他一点钱，”他微红着脸。“他不要，可我非让他收下。他又拥抱了我一下，然后把钱扔到一边去了。”

“很有可能，”赫伯特装出一副恐怖的样子，说道，“我们会变成百万富翁，会出名，会过上幸福生活。爸爸，第一个愿望是当皇帝吧，这样你就不会受管制了。”

说完，赫伯特围着桌子飞跑着，怀特太太夹着沙发套，生气地在后面追赶。

怀特先生从衣袋里掏出猴爪，怀疑地瞅着它。“说真的，我真不知道该许什么愿，”他慢慢地说道。“我想要的好像都得到了。”

“要是把房子打扫干净，你就会感到非常幸福，不是吗？”赫伯特说着，把手搭在父亲肩膀上。“所以，你就说希望得到两百英镑吧，这就可以用来打扫屋子了。”

父亲不好意思地笑着，笑他自己容易上当，他拿起猴爪，而他的儿子，则神情凝重，母亲朝他递眼色，打乱了他的表情，于是他坐下来，扣出几声响亮的和弦。

“我希望得到两百英镑。”老头响亮地说。

"It moved," he cried, with a glance of disgust at the object as it lay on the floor. "As I wished, it twisted in my hand like a snake."

"Well, I don't see the money," said his son, as he picked it up and placed it on the table, "and I bet I never shall."

"It must have been your fancy, father," said his wife, regarding him anxiously.

He shook his head. "Never mind, though; there's no harm done, but it gave me a shock all the same."

They sat down by the fire again while the two men finished their pipes. Outside, the wind was higher than ever, and the old man started nervously at the sound of a door banging upstairs. A silence unusual and depressing settled on all three, which lasted until the old couple rose to retire for the rest of the night.

"I expect you'll find the cash tied up in a big bag in the middle of your bed," said Herbert, as he bade them goodnight, "and something horrible squatting on top of your wardrobe watching you as you pocket your ill-gotten gains."

He sat alone in the darkness, gazing at the dying fire, and seeing faces in it. The last was so horrible and so simian that he gazed at it in amazement. It got so vivid that, with a little uneasy laugh, he felt on the table for a glass containig a little water to throw over it. His hand grasped the monkey's paw, and with a little shiver he wiped his hand on his coat and went up to bed.

钢琴发出美妙的声音来配合他的话，可是老人突然发出一声惊叫打断了琴声。妻子和儿子向他跑去。

“它动了，”他惊叫出声。猴爪正躺在地板上，他用厌恶的眼光盯着那个宝贝。“我刚才许愿时，它像蛇一样在我手里扭动起来。”

“是吗，我怎么没看到钱呢，”儿子说着，把猴爪捡起来，放在桌子上。“我敢打赌，咱们永远也看不到这笔钱。”

“这肯定是你的幻觉，他爸。”妻子担心地望着他，说道。

他摇摇头。“不要紧，反正它没有伤害我，可还是吓了我一跳。”

两个男人抽完烟，在壁炉边坐了下来。外面的风比任何时候都要大，楼上的房门突然响了一声，老头紧张地跳起来。三个人默不作声，气氛变得分外压抑。直到这对老夫妻都去睡觉了。

“我希望你会发现现金装在一个大口袋里，而口袋就在床中间，”赫伯特对父母道晚安时说，“有个怪兽会蹲在大衣柜上，看你有没有私吞这笔横财。”

他独自坐在黑暗中，望着即将熄灭的壁炉。壁炉里出现许多脸孔，最后一张面孔非常可怕，看起来特别熟悉。他惊讶地盯着这张面孔，它的模样很逼真，脸上带着一丝不安的微笑。他从桌子上抓起一个水杯，把剩下的一点水都浇进火里。他拿起那个猴爪，手微微颤抖。他把手在外套上擦了擦，转身睡觉去了。

The Monkey's Paw (Ⅱ)

猴爪（2）

◎ W. W. Jacobs

In the brightness of the wintry sun next morning as it streamed over the breakfast table he laughed at his fears. There was an air of prosaic wholesomeness about the room which it had lacked on the previous night, and the dirty, shriveled little paw was pitched on the side-board with a carelessness which betokened no great belief in its virtues.

"I suppose all old soldiers are the same," said Mrs. White. "The idea of our listening to such nonsense! How could wishes be granted in these days? And if they could, how could two hundred pounds hurt you, father?"

"Might drop on his head from the sky," said the frivolous Herbert.

"Morris said the things happened so naturally," said his father, "that you might if you so wished attribute it to coincedence."

"Well don't break into the money before I come back," said Herbert as he rose from the table. "I'm afraid it'll turn you into a mean, avaricious man, and we shall have to disown you."

His mother laughed, and following him to the door, watched him down

第二天早晨，当冬日的阳光倾洒在餐桌上，赫伯特开始嘲笑他的恐惧来。房间里的空气如平日里一样清新，跟昨晚大不相同。那个干瘪又脏兮兮的小猴爪斜放在餐具柜上，没有人留意，因为谁也不相信它的魔力。

“我猜，所有的老军人全都一样，”怀特太太说。“咱们怎么会相信这种胡说！这几天怎么能确定愿望会不会实现呢？他爸，如果它真的实现了，两百英镑又怎么能伤害你呢？”

“这笔钱大概会从天而降，砸在他脑袋上。”赫伯特轻佻地说。

“莫里斯说过，事情会发生得非常自然，”父亲说，“你也许会把它归之于巧合。”

“那好，在我回家之前，最好不要独吞这笔钱，”赫伯特说着，从桌边站起来，“我怕它会把你变成吝啬而贪婪的人，那样一来，我们就会和你断绝关系。”

母亲笑着，陪着儿子走到大门口，看着他走上马路，然后回到餐桌旁。

the road; and returning to the breakfast table, was very happy at the expense of her husband's credulity. All of which did not prevent her from scurrying to the door at the postman's knock, nor prevent her from referring somewhat shortly to retired Sergeant-Majors of bibulous habits when she found that the post brought a tailor's bill.

"Herbert will have some more of his funny remarks, I expect, when he comes home," she said as they sat at dinner.

"I dare say," said Mr. White, pouring himself out some beer; "but for all that, the thing moved in my hand; that I'll swear to."

"You thought it did," said the old lady soothingly.

"I say it did," replied the other. "There was no thought about it; I had just—What's the matter?"

His wife made no reply. She was watching the mysterious movements of a man outside, who, peering in an undecided fashion at the house, appeared to be trying to make up his mind to enter. In mental connexion with the two hundred pounds, she noticed that the stranger was well dressed, and wore a silk hat of glossy newness. Three times he paused at the gate, and then walked on again. The fourth time he stood with his hand upon it, and then with sudden resolution flung it open and walked up the path. Mrs. White at the same moment placed her hands behind her, and hurriedly unfastening the strings of her apron, put that useful article of apparel beneath the cusion of her chair.

She brought the stranger, who seemed ill at ease, into the room. He gazed at her furtively, and listened in a preoccupied fashion as the old lady apologized for the appearance of the room, and her husband's coat, a garment which he usually

丈夫因为轻信而付出了代价，她因此十分高兴。尽管如此，她还是不动声色地忙碌着。当邮差开始敲门时，她急忙跑到大门口去开门。看到邮差送来裁缝的账单，她又跟丈夫谈了几句退役的莫里斯嗜酒的坏习惯。

“我希望，赫伯特回家后还能再说几句有趣的话。”他们坐下吃晚餐时，她对丈夫说。

“我敢说，”怀特先生说着，给自己倒了一点啤酒，“一切都在我的掌控之中，这点我可以发誓。”

“这只是你自己的想法。”妻子安慰他说。

“没错，”丈夫回答，“我也没有胡思乱想，我只是……怎么了？”

妻子并没回答。她在观察屋外那个陌生人的神秘举动，他犹豫不决地窥视着他们的房子，似乎决定走进去。她心里想着那两百英镑，同时又见那人穿着不赖，头上还戴着崭新的缎面礼帽。他在门口停顿了三次，但每次都又继续向前走。当他第四次来到门口，站在那儿时，把手放在门上，突然把心一横，猛地推开门走了进去。看到这里，怀特太太立刻把双手放在背后，慌忙解开围裙的带子，把它压在椅垫下面。

她把陌生人领进来，他显得忐忑不安。老妇人为房间的凌乱和丈夫的脏外套道歉（那是他做园艺工作时穿的），陌生人偷偷地窥视着她，心事重重地听着。然后，她拿出女性的全部耐心，等待陌生人开口提出来访理由，

reserved for the garden. She then waited as patiently as her sex would permit for him to broach his business, but he was at first strangely silent.

"I—was asked to call," he said at last, and stooped and picked a piece of cotton from his trousers. "I come from 'Maw and Meggins'."

The old lady started. "Is anything the matter?" she asked breathlessly. "Has anything happened to Herbert? What is it? What is it?"

Her husband interposed, "There, there, mother," he said hastily. "Sit down, and don't jump to conclusions. You've not brought bad news, I'm sure sir," and eyed the other wistfully.

"I'm sorry—" began the visitor.

"Is he hurt?" demanded the mother wildly.

The visitor bowed in assent. "Badly hurt," he said quietly, "but he is not in any pain."

"Oh thank God!" said the old woman, clasping her hands. "Thank God for that! Thank—"

She broke off as the sinister meaning of the assurance dawned on her and she saw the awful confirmation of her fears in the others averted face. She caught her breath, and turning to her slower-witted husband, laid her trembling hand on his. There was a long silence.

"He was caught in the machinery," said the visitor at length in a low voice.

"Caught in the machinery," repeated Mr. White, in a dazed fashion, "yes."

He sat staring out the window, and taking his wife's hand between his own, pressed it as he had been wont to do in their old courting days nearly forty years before.

他却第一次出奇地沉默了。

“我……被派来通知你们，”最后，陌生人终于开口了。他弯下腰，摘掉裤子上的一片棉花，“我来自‘莫和梅吉恩’公司。”

老妇人很惊讶。“出什么事了吗？”她紧张地问，“赫伯特出了什么事？怎么样？他怎么样了？”

丈夫插嘴道：“孩子妈妈，”他急忙说，“坐下来，别忙着下结论。一定不是坏消息，我敢肯定，先生。”他渴望地瞅着陌生人。

“很抱歉……”陌生人说。

“他受伤了？”母亲疯一般地问。

陌生人鞠躬以示默认。“他伤得很厉害，”他平静地说，“可他没感到任何痛苦。”

“噢，感谢上帝！”老妇人十指交叉说道，“感谢上帝！感谢……”

她渐渐明白这番话的不祥含义，突然沉默下来。她的恐惧在陌生人别过去的脸上得到了印证。她屏住呼吸，转向比她更迟钝的丈夫，把颤抖的手放在他手心里。他们久久地沉默着。

“他被机器搅进去了。”最后，陌生人低声说。

“被机器搅进去了，”怀特先生茫然地重复着，“是的。”

他坐下来，望着窗外，把妻子的手夹在他的双手之间，就像近四十年前他们恋爱时那样。

"He was the only one left to us," he said, turning gently to the visitor. "It is hard."

The other coughed, and rising, walked slowly to the window. "The firm wishes me to covey their sincere sympathy with you in your great loss," he said, without looking round. "I beg that you will understand I am only their servant and merely obeying orders."

There was no reply; the old woman's face was white, her eyes staring, and her breath inaudible; on the husband's face was a look such as his friend the sergeant might have carried into his first action.

"I was to say that Maw and Meggins disclaim all responsibility," continued the other. "They admit no liability at all, but in consideration of your son's services, they wish to present you with a certain sum as compensation."

Mr. White dropped his wife's hand, and rising to his feet, gazed with a look of horror at his visitor. His dry lips shaped the words, "How much?"

"Two hundred pounds," was the answer.

Unconcious of his wife's shriek, the old man smiled faintly, put out his hands like a sightless man, and dropped, a senseless heap, to the floor.

“我们只剩下这一个孩子，”他说着，缓缓转向陌生人。“这个打击很残酷。”

陌生人咳了几声站起来，慢慢走到窗口，“公司希望我来转达真切的慰唁，对你们的巨大损失表示同情，”他头也不回地说，“我请求你们理解我，我只是公司的雇员，我之所以到这儿来，仅仅是为了服从命令。”

没有人回答他。老妇人脸色惨白，眼珠一动不动，听不到任何呼吸声。老头的表情非常复杂，他的军人朋友说到第一个许愿者死亡的时候，几乎也是这种表情。

“我要告诉你们，‘莫和梅吉恩’公司拒绝承担任何责任，”陌生人继续说，“因为他们认为公司毫无责任。不过，考虑到你儿子对公司作出的贡献，他们想要赠给你们一笔钱，以此作为补偿。”

怀特先生放开妻子的手，站起来，用可怕的眼神盯住陌生人，从干瘪的嘴唇里挤出两个字：“多少？”

“两百英镑。”陌生人回答。

老头没在意妻子的尖叫，脸上隐约透着笑意，他伸出双手，像盲人一样，颓然倒地。

The Monkey's Paw (Ⅲ)
猴爪（3）

◎ W. W. Jacobs

In the huge new cemetery, some two miles distant, the old people buried their dead, and came back to the house steeped in shadows and silence. It was all over so quickly that at first they could hardly realize it, and remained in a state of expectation as though of something else to happen—something else which was to lighten this load, too heavy for old hearts to bear.

But the days passed, and expectations gave way to resignation—the hopeless resignation of the old, sometimes mis-called apathy. Sometimes they hardly exchanged a word, for now they had nothing to talk about, and their days were long to weariness.

It was a about a week after that the old man, waking suddenly in the night, stretched out his hand and found himself alone. The room was in darkness, and the sound of subdued weeping came from the window. He raised himself in bed and listened.

"Come back," he said tenderly. "You will be cold."

"It is colder for my son," said the old woman, and wept afresh.

那是个巨大的新墓地，离家大约有两英里远。老人把儿子埋葬后回到家里，他们沉浸在忧戚和沉默之中。一切结束得这么快，他们还没回过神来，还期望着发生别的什么事——一些能减轻这重负的事，这于两颗苍老的心来说，实在不堪忍受。

日子一天天过去。期望渐渐变成了认命——他们绝望地认命，有时候会被误称为漠然。他们几乎一句话都不说，因为他们现在没什么可说的，消沉的日子太过漫长。

大约一周后，老头突然从夜里醒来。他伸手一摸，妻子不在身边。房间里黑漆漆的，窗户附近传来一阵轻微的啜泣声。他从床上坐起来，仔细倾听。

“回来睡觉吧，”他轻声说，“你会着凉的。”

“我儿子住的地方比这儿更冷。”老太婆说着，又啜泣起来。

她的啜泣声渐渐在他耳边消失。床很温暖，他两眼昏沉欲睡。他断断

The sounds of her sobs died away on his ears. The bed was warm, and his eyes heavy with sleep. He dozed fitfully, and then slept until a sudden wild cry from his wife awoke him with a start.

"The paw!" she cried wildly. "The monkey's paw!"

He started up in alarm. "Where? Where is it? What's the matter?"

She came stumbling across the room toward him. "I want it," she said quietly. "You've not destroyed it?"

"It's in the parlour, on the bracket," he replied, marveling. "Why?"

She cried and laughed together, and bending over, kissed his cheek.

"I only just thought of it," she said hysterically. "Why didn't I think of it before? Why didn't you think of it?"

"Think of what?" he questioned.

"The other two wishes," she replied rapidly. "We've only had one."

"Was not that enough?" he demanded fiercely.

"No," she cried triumphantly; "We'll have one more. Go down and get it quickly, and wish our boy alive again."

The man sat in bed and flung the bedcloths from his quaking limbs. "Good God, you are mad!" he cried aghast. "Get it," she panted; "get it quickly, and wish—Oh my boy, my boy!"

Her husband struck a match and lit the candle. "Get back to bed," he said unsteadily. "You don't know what you are saying."

"We had the first wish granted," said the old woman, feverishly; "why not the second?"

"A coincidence," stammered the old man.

续续地打着盹儿，后来就睡着了，直到被妻子的喊叫声惊醒。

“爪子！”她拼命地大喊，“猴爪！”

他被吓了一跳。“在哪儿？它在哪儿呢？出什么事了？”

她踉跄地穿过屋子走向丈夫。“我需要它，”她平静地说，“你没有弄坏它吧？”

“它在客厅的壁炉架上，”他不解地回答，“你要它干什么？”

她又哭又笑，俯下身子，亲吻丈夫。

“我刚刚想到它，”她异常激动地说。“为什么我以前没想到它？为什么你没想到？”

“想到什么？”他问。

“剩下的两个愿望呀，”她飞快地回答，“我们还有一个机会。”

“难道这还不够吗？”他难过地说。

“当然不够，”她得意地大叫，“我们可以许个更好的愿望。起来，快去拿猴爪，让我们的儿子复活。”

老头坐起来，从颤抖的四肢上掀开被子，“上帝呀，你疯了！”他惊慌地大叫，“快去拿，”她气喘吁吁地说，“快去拿它，然后再许个愿……噢，儿子，我的儿子！”

丈夫划起一根火柴，点燃蜡烛。“上床睡觉去，”他哆哆嗦嗦地说，“你都不知道自己在说些什么。”

“我们的第一个愿望实现了，”老妇人兴奋地说，“为什么不试试第二个

"Go get it and wish," cried his wife, quivering with excitement.

The old man turned and regarded her, and his voice shook. "He has been dead ten days, and besides he—I would not tell you else, but—I could only recognize him by his clothing. If he was too terrible for you to see then, how now?"

"Bring him back," cried the old woman, and dragged him towards the door. "Do you think I fear the child I have nursed?"

He went down in the darkness, and felt his way to the parlour, and then to the mantlepiece. The talisman was in its place, and a horrible fear that the unspoken wish might bring his mutillated son before him ere he could escape from the room seized up on him, and he caught his breath as he found that he had lost the direction of the door. His brow cold with sweat, he felt his way round the table, and groped along the wall until he found himself in the small passage with the unwholesome thing in his hand.

Even his wife's face seemed changed as he entered the room. It was white and expectant, and to his fears seemed to have an unnatural look upon it. He was afraid of her.

"Wish!" she cried in a strong voice.

"It is foolish and wicked," he faltered.

"Wish!" repeated his wife.

He raised his hand. "I wish my son alive again."

The talisman fell to the floor, and he regarded it fearfully. Then he sank trembling into a chair as the old woman, with burning eyes, walked to the window and raised the blind.

呢？”

“那是……巧合。”老头结结巴巴地说。

“去，去拿它，然后再许个愿。”老太婆激动得全身发颤。

老头转身看着她，声音有些发抖，“他已经死了十天了，此外，他……我真不愿意对你说这个，可是……现在我只能够认出他的衣服。假如他的模样让你恐惧，那该怎么办？”

“把他带回来，”老太婆大喊，还一边把老头往门口方向拉，“你认为，我会害怕我养大的孩子吗？”

老头走进黑暗中，摸着黑来到客厅，走向壁炉架。那个宝贝还在，他非常害怕，唯恐那个没说出口的愿望把肢体残缺不全的儿子带到面前，自己还来不及逃走就会被他捉住。他忽然找不到门在哪儿了，于是屏住了呼吸，额头渗出冷汗来。他绕着桌子摸索着，沿着墙边摸索。最后，他发现自己站在狭窄的走廊里，手里抓着那个害人的东西。

当他回到房间，发现就连妻子的脸也变得非常可怕。她脸色惨白，充满期待，眼神也似乎不太正常，看起来让人害怕。他害怕她。

“许愿！”她大声叫道。

“这是愚蠢而邪恶的事。”他结结巴巴地说。

“许愿！”妻子重复道。

他举起手。“我想要我的儿子复活。”

那个宝贝跌落到地板上，他恐惧地盯看它。然后，他颤颤巍巍地陷进

He sat until he was chilled with the cold, glancing occasionally at the figure of the old woman peering through the window. The candle-end, which had burned below the rim of the china candlestick, was throwing pulsating shadows on the ceiling and walls, until with a flicker larger than the rest, it expired. The old man, with an unspeakable sense of relief at the failure of the talisman, crept back to his bed, and a minute afterward the old woman came silently and apathetically beside him.

Neither spoke, but lay silently listening to the ticking of the clock. A stair creaked, and a squeaky mouse scurried noisily through the wall. The darkness was oppressive, and after lying for some time screwing up his courage, he took the box of matches, and striking one, went downstairs for a candle.

At the foot of the stairs the match went out, and he paused to strike another; and at the same moment a knock came so quiet and stealthy as to be scarcely audible, sounded on the front door.

The matches fell from his hand and spilled in the passage. He stood motionless, his breath suspended until the knock was repeated. Then he turned and fled swiftly back to his room, and closed the door behind him. A third knock sounded through the house.

"What's that?" cried the old woman, starting up.

"A rat," said the old man in shaking tones—"a rat. It passed me on the stairs."

His wife sat up in bed listening. A loud knock resounded through the house.

"It's Herbert!"

She ran to the door, but her husband was before her, and catching her by the

椅子里。老妇人眼睛发亮，她走到窗前，拉起了百叶窗。

他坐在那儿，冷得发抖，偶尔看看老妇人望着窗外的身影。蜡烛已经燃到尽头，火苗在陶瓷烛台的边缘跳动，影子被投射到天花板和墙壁上，跳动着。最后，火苗猛地蹿起来，然后完全熄灭了。老头回到床上，宝贝的失灵让他感受到一种无法言说的释然，一分钟后，老妇人默默回到床上，漠然地在他身边躺了下来。

两个人都没说话，他们静静地躺着，倾听时钟的滴答声。楼梯上发出吱吱的响动，一只老鼠尖声叫着，迅速跑过墙边。黑暗让人十分压抑。躺了一段时间之后，老头鼓起勇气，拿出火柴．划着一根，下楼去找蜡烛。

火柴在楼梯口熄灭了。他停住脚，又划了一根火柴。与此同时，大门口传来敲门声，声音鬼鬼祟祟，轻得几乎听不出来。

火柴从老头手里掉下去，落在过道上。他面目表情地站在那儿，直到敲门声再次响起，他才得以呼出气来。接下来，他转过身，飞速跑回房间，回身关好房门。第三次敲门声回荡在房子里。

“什么声音？”老太婆喊着，坐了起来。

“耗子，”老头用颤抖的声音说，“一只耗子。它从我身边跑过，上了楼梯。”

妻子坐在床上听。响亮的敲门声，在房子里回荡。

“是赫伯特！”

arm, held her tightly.

"What are you going to do?" he whispered hoarsely.

"It's my boy; it's Herbert!" she cried, struggling mechanically. "I forgot it was two miles away. What are you holding me for? Let go. I must open the door."

"For God's sake don't let it in," cried the old man, trembling.

"You're afraid of your own son," she cried struggling. "Let me go. I'm coming, Herbert; I'm coming."

There was another knock, and another. The old woman with a sudden wrench broke free and ran from the room. Her husband followed to the landing, and called after her appealing as she hurried downstairs. He heard the chain rattle back and the bolt drawn slowly and stiffly from the socket. Then the old woman's voice, strained and panting.

"The bolt," she cried loudly. "Come down. I can't reach it."

But her husband was on his hands and knees groping wildly on the floor in search of the paw. If only he could find it before the thing outside got in. A perfect fusillade of knocks reverberated through the house, and he heard the scraping of a chair as his wife as his wife put it down in the passage against the door. He heard the creaking of the bolt as it came slowly back, and at the same moment he found the monkey's paw, and frantically breathed his third and last wish.

The knocking ceased suddenly, although the echoes of it were still in the house. He heard the chair drawn back, and the door opened. A cold wind rushed

她向门口跑去，丈夫却拦在她面前，紧紧地攥住她的胳膊。

“你要干什么？”他沙哑地低语。

“是我儿子在敲门，是赫伯特！”她大喊，机械地挣扎着。“我忘了，墓地离这儿有两英里远呢。你干吗抓着我？放手。我说什么也要去开门。”

“看在上帝份上，别让它进来。”老头哆哆嗦嗦地大叫。

“你居然害怕自己的儿子，”她大叫，继续挣扎。“放开我。赫伯特！我来了，妈妈来了！”

敲门声又响起了。突然，老太婆猛地挣脱手臂，跑出房间。丈夫追着她来到楼梯平台处，求她回来，她却急忙地奔向楼下。老头听见摘下链子的哗啦声，门闩也被缓缓拔出。接着，他听到妻子紧张而喘息的声音。

“门闩，”她大叫，“来帮帮我呀。我够不着它。”

可是丈夫四脚着地，拼命地在地板上摸索，寻找那个猴爪。要是能够在那个东西从外面进来之前找到它就好了。连续的敲门声不断地在房子里回响。妻子从走廊里拖出一把椅子，放到门后，老头能听见椅子在地板上的摩擦声。老头听到门闩被慢慢拉开的声音，这时，他突然摸到猴爪，立刻声嘶力竭地说出第三个，也是最后一个愿望。

敲门声突然停止，但回声仍在房子里回旋。老头听见椅子被拉开的声

up the staircase, and a long loud wail of disappointment and misery from his wife gave him the courage to run down to her side, and then to the gate beyond. The streetlamp flickering opposite shone on a quiet and deserted road.

音。大门打开了，寒风扑向楼梯，妻子发出一阵长长的、交织着痛苦和失望的哀号。妻子的声音给了老头勇气，他跑到她身边，然后又来到门外。街灯在对面闪光，路上静悄悄的，空无一人。

There are two sides to every story...at least.

每个故事都可以从两个方面看，至少两个方面。